DUBLIN...1972

Dublin...1972

ISBN 978-1-912606-04-7

Printed in Ireland by Lettertec

lettertec

About the Author

Marty Power was born in Walkinstown on the south side of Dublin in 1956. He emigrated to Perth in Western Australia with his wife Caroline, son Gary and daughter Gillian. This is his first book.

Marty's biggest passions, besides his family, are Manchester United, U2, David Bowie and Gilbert O'Sullivan. He hopes this won't put anyone off reading his book...☺

The author would like to acknowledge Angela Williamson for her cover design and the handsome Brandon Guest who features on it. He would also like to give huge thank you to Andrew and everyone from Lettertec for their amazing patience over the last few years.

If you would like to contact the author, he can be reached at his website **www.dublin1972.com**

Acknowledgement:

Thank you Joan and Tony for this mind that doesn't know when to stop.

And Caroline, Gary and Gillian for putting up with it. And Sheelagh and Terry for being part of my voyage up to now.....and Brian who told me to write this book...........lest we forget the way we were.

Hold on to sixteen as long as you can

Changes come around real soon make us women and men.

John Cougar, *Jack and Diane, 1982.*

Contents

June 1972

"He's a fuckin' queer" Tony informed us.

"Did ye see the clobber on him? Like bleedin' pyjamas."

We then got a rendering of a verse of the song he sang:

"There's a Starman waitin' in the sky...."

"Shut up!" I said. "I think he's great. He's goin' to be real big."

"Yeah, about six foot six" Mick said and we all laughed.

"Did yi see the bleedin' hair on him? Like a toilet brush!! What was his name?" Tony asked.

"David Bowie" I said.

"David fuckin' Bumboy" Tony said.

"Look, you don't like him and I do OK? Do yi remember that song a few years ago "Ground Control to Major Tom? Well he sung that, OK?"

"Did he? Yeah, I remember that." Des said with a belch on the word "remember".

He was super at that, belchin' and talking at the same time. Passing the B & I office we all turned left to look at ourselves in the window. Bleedin' cool. Doc Martens, two-tones, black Harrington jackets, check shirts, braces and very little hair, although we would have spent half the day getting the hair right. We felt on top of the world. All around Westmoreland Street, O'Connell Street, Dame Street and Capel Street, little groups like ourselves were heading out on a Friday night in June 1972 to one of the half a dozen dances going on in the city. Not a worry in the world except maybe how much reggae would the DJ play? Would that mot with the black hair and black Doc's look at me again and would we even get in with the smell of Bulmers on our breaths?

"I'm burstin' for a slash" Tommy said.

On the other side of the bridge we went up a lane and pissed up against Smallman's wall. Tony caught his mickey in his zip. He pretended it didn't hurt and went into a corner to free it.

"This is no place to be playin' with yourself" this CIE busman said as he passed him.

We all broke our bollox laughing.

"Ha ha, very bleedin' funny" Tony said.

Tony always looked the smartest of us all. He was the tallest. His fair hair, although cut very short, made him look like Michael Caine. He had these bright red braces that he pulled up so tight his two-tones were always bet up his arse. We were all good looking in our own individual way, and we knew it. We could have had anyone we wanted. Most of us had a girlfriend, but on a Friday night we went out on our own. A flagon each in Mooney's field, 10 Major and you were made. Jesus, it was great being sixteen. Nearly a year left school, money in your sky rocket, a nice looking mot and the best of clothes and of course respect. Respect was so important. The last thing you wanted to be was ordinary. That was for other gobshites. We were special.

"Errol or Preh?"

"Did he mean Herald or Press boys?" I said in a posh Dublin accent.

We all knew what he said though. He was a Dub and so were we. Another quick look at ourselves in Eason's window. Tony looked shattered all of a sudden!

"Ah bollox, look at me fuckin' strides."

He has pissed on the front of them. Not much, but on a pair of bright green two-tones it really showed up.

"Tony, you won't notice it in the Loft, it's so dark anyway" I said.

"Could be bleedin' worse" said Mick, "your mickey could still be caught in your zip as well!"

More laughter.

We all burst into Song "*Metal Guru, is it you? Yeah, yeah, yeah, Metal Guru is it you? Yeah, yeah, yeah...*"

Shit. Around the corner from Henry Street came pure trouble, about fifteen of them. These situations always brought us down to earth. They could eat us up and spit us out in fifteen seconds flat. Nearly everyone had a bald head. They always looked like those people behind the wire in the photographs of the concentrations camps. Poor. Donkey jackets, turned up cheap jeans and black boots. From some flats somewhere. We stood out like spare pricks with our cool gear, straight from England.

If anyone was going to England for a holiday they were given a few quid to bring us back something different. Something that the crappy Capel Street clothes shops wouldn't have in stock for at least a year. From five happy smiling faces to five pallbearers in less than a second.

This is it. They're going to beat the shite out of the five of us and rob all our clothes. I'm going to have to walk home from O'Connell Street naked.

"Have yi got a smoke, pal?" the toughest looking one asked.

Des immediately took out his Major and gave him one, expecting the packet to be snatched out of his hand. He had the most horrible face of pimples I had ever seen. Pure ugly. The rest of the animals stood behind him as if waiting for a signal.

"Where yi from?"

"Walkinstown" Tony said.

I always stood behind in these situations. If the digs were going to be issued I would be the first to run! When it came to aggro we usually shit ourselves, although Mick could take care of himself.

"Do yi know John Donnelly?" pimple-face asked.

"Do you mean John Donnelly who works in the CIE works in Inchicore?" Tony asked.

"That's him. I work there too."

Relief. We indirectly knew the animal gang. A small conversation followed about where we were going, where we got our clobber and so on. Des asked if anyone else would like a cigarette but a little skinhead with tattoo on his arm said "Ah, no thanks. Yi haven't got many left".

My God, they had feelings! The fact that crater face knew somebody we knew changed the whole situation. We were pals. We were happy. We could have brought them all home for tea!

"See yi again, pal" and we were all on our way. You felt like somebody just freed from prison.

"Where did he say they were goin'?" I said.

"The Go-Go Club" Tommy said. "Did yi see his mush? Imagine Donnelly has to look at him all day. Eatin' your lunch and havin' to look at the shaggin' big pimples."

"Ah, Jaysus, I'm goin' to be sick even thinkin' about it" Mick said.

"I thought they were going to beat the shite out of us" said Tommy.

"They wouldn't have to" Tony said. "If one of his pimples had exploded the whole of O'Connell Street would be dead".

More laughter. Des laughed so much he sunk down on his hunkers outside the Carlton. We loved a good laugh.

"Jaysus, look at who it is Marty" Des said.

These two birds came towards us. Tartan skirts, black nylons, black shoes, v-neck woolen jumpers and check shirts, hair as short as ours, pretending not to see us.

"Tony" said Des "look who it is. It's smelly arse".

"Oh shit" said Tony.

Tony had left the one on the outside home to Cabra a few months ago and on the bus she farted. Tony in his own ways was prudish and it really shocked him. That was the end of the short relationship. They passed by never looking at us once. Tommy made a fart noise.

"Shut the fuck up, will yi" Tony said. "We could have been talkin' to their brothers a few minutes ago. Every time I think of that night! If yis don't laugh I'll tell yi the truth. OK?"

"OK" we said, walking all in line now. "Tell us what happened".

"I never knew women could fart. I never once heard me Ma or sister fartin'".

"You're jokin'" I said. "They have arses like us, haven't they?"

"I never heard me Ma either" Tommy said.

"I often heard me Da" I said. "When we were kids if a cowboy film was on, me Da would point his finger like a gun and when the Indians came on he'd let out a huge one. Me Ma would go mad but we'd break our shite laughin'."

Da would do that. He would create some form of fun for a brief period and we'd all laugh our arses off, Ma and all. The culchies next door never laughed.

They always looked real serious, every time you saw them. You never heard any noise at all coming out of their house. Me Da reckoned it was because they only had RTE. He reckoned there was nothing on RTE to make you laugh. Not like the BBC and UTV that we had. The next day you would think of something you saw on telly the night before and you would be laughin' again, but they had nothing to laugh about, Ma said they were like people who emigrated. They lived in Dublin but they really didn't want to be here. You always knew it was springtime when tons of cow shite would appear outside their house all of a sudden. Da would be disgusted, especially with the smell in the street.

"Jaysus, imagine all the fun they'd be missin' if they couldn't fart" said Tommy.

"Did yi see the news this evenin' about the explosion in Belfast?" I asked.

"Aw, yeah" said Des. "Your man with the shovel?. Jaysus."

"It looked like what we put in the bins every evening" Tony said.

Tony was a butcher's apprentice.

"It must have been some bleedin' bomb. He just shoveled it into a plastic bag?" Des said. "They always show yi these things when you're havin' your tea. Some poor bollox went out to do some shoppin' and ends up on the end of a shovel being put into a plastic bag."

We all went quiet. Two hours away they were killing each other and we were heading off for an evening of fun.

"They're all mad up there" said Tommy. "I'm glad I live in Dublin. There's two of them working on our site and everyone's afraid of them. They're alright though. One of them was in school with Georgie Best." He's Manchester United mad.

Tommy was an apprentice carpenter. He always had that timbery smell of him, like you always got in Chadwick's timber shop. If we went out for a night, he always had the exact money with him for everything, down to the chips on the way home. He had it figured out precisely. If something different happened on the night, like us buying twenty Major instead of 10 or a large single instead of a small, he'd have a really worried look on his face. He had been working on the same site since he started the apprenticeship and every evening he took home a sack of sticks for his Ma for the fire. He was a funny bastard though. You could say anything to him. Anyone who came home on the 50 bus every evening with the same sack full of sticks must have a hard neck.

Around by the pregnancy hospital loads of little groups like us were heading in the same direction.

"Why do they call it Parnell Square? Who the hell was Parnell?"

"Probably the patron Saint of women who have babies" said Des.

"No, yi gobshite. He was a famous politician" I said. "All the Dublin streets are called after famous people."

"Jaysus, I never knew that" said Des.

"Then who the fuck was Abbey?" said Tommy. "Lower Abbey Streeet, Upper Abbey Street. He must have been very special".

"No, they cut him in half and called 2 streets after him" said Des.

All the little groups looked over at us. They had that "Why are they so happy?" look on their faces. I loved that about us all. We had wit at will.

"Jaysus, I'm burstin' again" said Tommy.

On the queue with the rest of the dudes. That fat bollox on the door again. We had come here every week for nearly a year, he knew us all well, but still went on as if we have never been here before.

"No weapons, no drink, no startin' fights and I hope you're all over sixteen".

Tony wasn't sixteen until September but you'd never know. We were all born in 1956. Tommy, the oldest, then me, then Des, Mick and Tony. Everybody smokin' to get rid of the smell of drink. I'm sure they knew but they would have had to bar just about everyone if they wanted to come the heavy.

Jesus, there she is again. About three people in front of me, Patricia O'Byrne. She was an absolute beauty. I was six months going out with Catherine Dwyer but she was never allowed out on a Friday night. She was lovely too but I was so bleedin' cocky I knew I could start going with any mot I wanted. The only problem was she was from Palmerstown and to me that was like being from Hong Kong. What if I started going out with her and I had to leave her home? Two shaggin' buses. I'd known Catherine since we were kids. Deep down I love her but yi know yourself! Tommy's eyes were starting to water over. He started breathing real quick. You could see he was really bursting. In we go. That complete buzz hit immediately. The ultra violet lights showed up all your dandruff, when you smiled you liked like a donkey with a mouthful of white teeth. Everybody looking at everybody, everyone throwing shapes.

"Aw great" said Tony "Ron is the DJ".

Ron was a John Lennon lookalike who played brilliant music. You could ask him to play a song and you knew he would. Not like the other swines who stick tapes on with their favourite songs.

We all moved around. Tommy headed straight for the jacks. The slow set started. That was the time you could see who was going with who. *"Alone Again, Naturally"*. I loved Gilbert. Like Bowie, he was different. Des was chatting up a mot already. He was the smallest of us all. He had a girlfriend who lived just three doors away from him but it wasn't really serious because her Da had applied to go to Australia and he knew it could end anytime. He hated talking about it. At sixteen emotions run very high, much higher than people think.

Des worked in Jacobs biscuit factory as an apprentice fitter. His Da had the first Ford Anglia ever bought in Ireland in his garage, still in great nick. If you wanted to see it, his Da always had to be there. Des said it would be worth a fortune someday.

Jaysus, he was getting' his wear off her. Piss time. Tony and Tommy were in the jacks talking to Ron the DJ.

"Have yi got *"Mother and Child Reunion* with yi' Ron? It's great for dancin'" Tony said.

"Yep, I'll play it soon" said Ron. "Where do you lot get all your gear from?" Ron asked.

"Well I got me Doc's from England" I said. "Me sister Joan was in Leicester at Easter and got them for £3.75. I got the Harrington jacket from a bloke I work with for five quid".

"I got mine in Liverpool in the Army and Navy Stores in April" Tony said. "We went over on the boat for the weekend and saw Liverpool play Arsenal in their last match of the season. I wish I'd had more money with me, they have some great gear there".

"Ron, have you got a minute?" fat bollox asked.

"See yis later, boys".

"See yi Ron".

"Nice guy isn't he?" I said.

"Fuckin' great" they agreed.

"Did yi see Des?" I asked.

"He doesn't waste his time does he?" said Tommy. "He'll be getting his hole next".

"What in the name of Jaysus does that mean?" I said pointing to the cistern over the urinal.

"Ziggy and the Spiders" was written all over it with a marker. It must mean something.

Back to the semi-darkness.

"Can you smell it?" said Tony.

"Yi dirty swine" I said.

"No yi gobshite. The Bob Hope. Smell it, someone' smokin'".

That distinct smell. Tommy Gleeson, his brother Sean and Paul McCarney. Everywhere they went they smoked dope. Even in school they were experimenting with dope. One night in Mooney's field I watched them "rolling a joint" as they used to say. It took McCarney about half an hour to make one. He put it into a silver paper, lit a match under it, mixed it with the tobacco from a Player's cigarette paper and licked it.He reckoned Player's made the best joints. Then he let the whole thing fall all over the grass. Tony looked at me and we coiled up laughing for at least ten minutes. McCarney reckoned he dropped it because we were looking at him.

As soon as Alice Cooper came on with *"Schools Out"* the three of them were up on the floor playing their imaginary guitars. Into the shop for a Coke and a packet of Tayto. Mick and Tommy were in the corner whispering to each other.

"C'mon" Tony said "no secrets".

"It's not a secret" said Tommy. "Yi know that bird with the short black hair from Palmerstown?"

"Yeah"

"She told her friend she's not going home tonight until she gets off with you".

"Me?" I said. "You're joking".

Shit. I couldn't do it on Catherine. Jaysus, if she found out.

"She's lovely though, isn't she? How do you pair know this?"

"Margaret Mooney told us".

Margaret Mooney was a gossip merchant. If you wanted the whole of Ireland to know something you didn't go to the Evening Herald, you told Margaret.

"The only thing is Marty, you'll never get the chance again" said Tommy, real philosophical like.

Some gobshite beside us was putting Aspro's in his Coke and shakin' the shite out of the bottle.

"What are yi doing that for?" Tommy said.

"Yi get high from it" he said.

"Fuck, I must try that" said Tony.

Mick farted. A sudden rush back to the dance floor. *"What's he like Mavis.... he's a real tasty geezer.?"* came over the speakers. The five of us up on the floor in a circle. We loved reggae. It was great dancing music. Secretly we like most music but we were totally into reggae as were most skinheads or suedeheads as we were called. Des came over with his mot.

"How are yis?" she said.

"This is Barbara" said Des, in his best Dublin accent.

She had a denim jacket with a Chelsea emblem sewn on to the pocket. She started dancing with us.

All of a sudden there was uproar. A row. A big circle formed with two eejits wrestling on the floor.

"Kick him in the bollox" this scrubber was screamin' at one of them.

All the lights came on and the two of them were dragged outside. That was the end of their night. From the corner of my eye I could see the beaut from Palmerstown looking at me. What will I do? Go with her for the night? But Palmerstown? No, shag that.

"There's that song again" Tony said. *"There's a starman waiting in the sky...."*

I love it. This was so different, I had to ask Ron.

"He's good isn't he?"

"Bowie, yeah. Do yi like him?"

"Yeah."

"You should get his album then. It's called "Ziggy Stardust and the Spiders from Mars".

So that's what the scribble in the jacks means!

"Yi not going to ask her up Marty?" Tony asked.

"No, it'll get back to Catherine. Its' not worth it."

Des sat down beside us, all happy looking.

"I'm going to leave her home. She lives in Drimnagh. I'll see yis tomorrow."

"Be a good boy now" Tony said "and if you cant' be good, be careful."

"Let's go, will we?" Tony asked.

"Yeah. I'll get Tommy and Mick" I said.

Mick was sitting with Tommy Gleeson smokin' some dope.

"We're goin'" I said "I'm in work tomorrow."

On the way out Margaret Mooney called me over and said "Are yi not going to even say hello to her?"

"Mind your own business" I said.

"Fuck off you, you're bleedin' full of yourself."

Yeah I am, I thought to myself. I am.

Back down O'Connell Street.

"Lets get a Wimpy" Tony said.

"Yeah, why not?" I'm starving, I thought.

The cider always make you hungry, That's why me Man and Dad always came in with chips after the pub. Upstairs into Wimpys. A table full of skinhead and suedehead girls were staring. Act casual. We sat at the table next to them. Pretend they're not there.

"Are you working tomorrow Marty?" Tony asked.

"Yeah, just half the day. I'm out in a computer centre in Cabinteely. It's just finished. There's heaps of scrap copper stashed behind a shed and we have to get it out on the sly. The plumber says whatever gosh we get from the scrapyard he'll give me a third."

"Jaysus, that's great" Mick said. "I've to knock down a wall with me Da in me Uncle Don's house in Rathmines" he said. "They're building an extension. Me Auntie Eileen's mad though. She has this depression thing."

"What the fuck does that mean?" Tommy asked.

"I think it's something wrong with her nerves" I said.

"Me Ma's sister, me Auntie Betty has it" said Tony. "She stays in bed all the time and she's always cryin'. Once she took too many tablets and had to go to hospital in an ambulance, I'd say it's something to do with women having babies or somethin'. They have to hide all the gargle in the house or she'll drink the lot."

"I'm glad I'm not a woman. They always seem to have these problems, with bleedin' periods and all."

Baldy Bertha at the next table was listening to us talking.

"Jesus we've got the problem page sittin' next to us. "Dear Frankie, I don't get periods, isn't it great."

Tony's face went tomato red. Me and Tommy took a fit of laughing till the tears rolled down our faces. The table of girls started laughing too, then Tony started laughing. The ice was broken. Yap Yap Yap for a while and we're off home.

"Imagine bringing that big baldy one home to meet your Ma & Da. They'd shoot yi'" Tommy said.

"I thought she was really funny though" I said. "Dear Frankie."

"You shut up" Tony said.

Fleet Street, packed as usual. Hundreds waiting on buses to take them home from the city to the south side of Dublin. The "50" isn't in yet so we stand and watch the parade of Friday night Dubs going home. A row starts on the back of the 56 bus.

Screamin' and roarin'. It was always great to watch but if you were involved you could end up in a bad fucking state. It usually started over the mere fact that you came from a different area than them. It was a territorial thing. Like animals. Two big culchie Gardai tear up the stairs to sort it out.

"I wonder how Des is getting on?" Tommy asks.

In came the 50. A queue, what queue? Mad rush to the back of the bus. You took your life into your hands getting on the bus in Dublin at any form of rush hour. Upstairs to the back seats.

A quick search down the back of the seats for money. Tony found a French letter.

"Someone's not getting their hole tonight" he laughs.

In front of us sits these two 'oul' ones and their men. Pissed. You instinctively knew they were going to be fun. The big woman looks all around her. Then she's off...

"*My old man says follow the van and don't do your danny on the way...* "

"Do your danny?? Tony looks at me and mimed "do your danny." Hysterics. The four of us with heads between our knees.

"What's so bloody funny. I suppose you four Osmond Brothers have a whole repertoire for us?"

"*I've been through the desert on a horse with no name, it felt good to be out of the rain...*"

Then we had the whole upstairs singing.

"*Na na na, Na na na na....*"

At the Barn the bus went over the canal and a brick hit the back window.

"Jaysus, bloody animals" the fat lady roared.

Tony still going "*After Nine days, I let the horse run free...* "

"Fares please".

You handed the conductor your fare and said "go ahead". No ticket, straight into his pocket. Fat lady's hubby was asleep and snoring. Her friend looked at him and said "Jaysus Agnes, you're in for a night of passion with Arthur, what?" She started laughing and her false teeth fell into her lap. Her whole face seemed to cave in. She looked like me granny.

"Oh stop Martha. For God's sake, or I'll never get me teeth back in".

I looked out the window at Crumlin Hospital. All the fun and noise going on in our bus and loads of little kids sick in bed. I'd been through it myself three or four times. I had an ingrown toe nail removed when I was seven and spent two weeks there. The boy next me had been in a big car crash and was bandaged all over. My job was to scratch him when he was itchy. His name was Fergal and was from the bog. A daunting place for a little kid. My brother Derek was 18 months old when he was brought in with Gastro Enteritis, me Ma was crying and we couldn't go into the room to see him in case we would give him more germs. So we all had to stand outside in a garden and look in through the window. Me Ma and Da, me brother and sister and me all crying. When the day came to bring him home, me Da gave him a jockey back from the hospital all the way to our house and had a big party.

All of us off the bus at the police station. Mick and Tommy lived in Crumlin, me and Tony in Walkinstown.

"See yis tomorrow."

Des lived in Crumlin too. Walkin' home with Tony we went thru the village. Past the shops and pubs. Always gangs on every corner.

"Got any odds?"

Always looking for money. People spilling out of the pubs onto the streets. In the back of your mind you know violence could erupt at any minute, yet there was singing everywhere. The chip shop queue went down past the butchers shop. Me Da was on the queue and gave me a wave.

"Shit, I better get home and mill into the toothpaste Tony" I said.

"Ah, me bollox, they know we drink. I'm sure they did when they were 16."

"I'm sure they did. But as me Da always said to me "I don't want you makin' the same mistakes I made."

So you always had to at least try to fool them.

"See yi tomorrow Tony."

"Yeah OK. Are you meetin' Catherine tomorrow night?"

"Yeah. I probably will. I might go to the pictures."

I loved our road. I lived just around the corner from Tony but our road had everything. A playing field where many an F.A. cup Final, World Cup Final and All Ireland Final was won or lost. Most houses had hedging. At the end of summer we used to set them on fire. The fire brigade would be called and there would be great commotion on the road. Nobody would know who did it but me and David would be stared at for weeks. Especially by the culchies. Their kids could do no wrong. Always studying for the big Civil Service job while us Dublin gutties were roaming the streets. Every second house had a Cherry Blossom tree in the front garden.

A few houses had a porch built on to the front. We had one that was packed with pot plants and umbrellas. The key was always behind the ivy plant. I sneaked in to see what David was up to with his girlfriend Alice. They heard me opening the inside door and you could hear the scatter in the back room. I loved doing that. They always babysat Derek on Friday night and if you sneaked in you would always catch them either rolling around on the settee or on the floor. David was a year younger than me and was what we called a hippie. He had an Afghan coat, long hair and put this perfume on called Patchulli which smelled like cats piss. He loved Jethro Tull, Jimi Hendrix, the Doors and all that shite. He had just done his Inter Cert and wanted to leave school and get a trade like me. Alice was the same, wore loads of long cheesecloth dresses and boots and floppy hats and loved Lindisfarne and Judy Collins. I could immediately smell the Bob Hope when I went into the back room.

"David, yi gobshite. Da's at the chipper and I can smell that stuff everywhere."

Back door and window opened immediately, dog runs under the settee, knows something's up. Towels fanned all over the room, ashtrays emptied into the bin and Alice sprays hair spray all over the room.

"Jaysus don't do that near the fire" I said.

Key in the front door. In comes Ma and Da. Three innocent children, watching the Friday night movie.

"Evening all, want some chips?"

Ma buttering the batch loaf in the kitchen.

"What's the smell?" says Da.

"It's hairspray Mr Curran. I'm trying to get the ends of my hair to stay down" says Alice.

Nice one Alice!

"What's on the telly?" asks Da.

"It's an old movie Mr Curran. The Treasure of the Sierra Madre it's called."

"That's a brilliant movie. Bogart's in it, isn't he?"

Ma singing in the kitchen *"All my life's a circle, sunrise and sundown..."*

She's a great singer. They always went to the singing pubs at the weekend and if there was a talent competition, Ma would enter it. She won a week in Butlins in 1968 for a family. Before the chips and bread are on the plates Da's asleep.

"That's a great song Marty. Have you heard it? It's by the New Seekers."

"Yeah, it's not bad Ma."

"They've been playing it all week on the radio. Bet yi' it gets to No.1. Where did you to tonight Marty?" she asks.

"We went to the Loft in Parnell Square."

"Was Catherine with yi'? Wake up Tony."

"No Ma, I'm seeing her tomorrow, going to the flix."

"God, look at that!" David says.

Late News. This little Vietamese kid running down a road with no clothes on and burns all over her, soldiers all around her, Napalm bombs going off down the road behind her.

"The poor girl. Jesus, we don't know how lucky we are" says Ma. "What the hell is that war over anyway?"

"Communists Ma" I said. "The North Vietnamese are Communists and the South are with the Yanks. The Americans don't even want to be there."

"Did yi see the bomb in Belfast today?" Alice says. "They said there was no warning. I think four or five were killed."

"There was a bomb scare in the city tonight" Dad says, one eye open, the other closed. "I heard a fella in the pub talking about it. They had to clear the Savoy cinema."

"I never saw anything in town" I said. "I'm going to bed. Goodnight."

"Did yi make your lunch?"

"Ah, Ma. I'll make it in the morning."

Me, David and Derek shared the front room. Joan had the small room or the "Box" room as it was called and me Ma and Da had the back room. My wall was covered in posters. T Rex, Slade, Gilbert O'Sullivan and the Rolling Stones. Since I was a kid, with my tranny under the covers listening to Radio Luxembourg, I loved the Stones. A year before, when I left school, Brown Sugar was No 1 so every time I heard it I had nothing but happy memoires. I fucking hated school. I couldn't believe it when I left. I was free. The Christian Brothers were OK but the teachers, who came in every day with their bad humours, and then started taking it out on us pissed me off. I used to spend half the day in school imaging me coming back when I was much older with a hurley stick and beating the shite out of them all. We had a lovely Maths teacher, Mr O'Byrne. Every Friday he would just sit there and talk to us like human beings. I liked him.

I opened the venetian blinds and looked out onto the road. Nearly every house had a metal railing separating their garden from the path. Only one or two had taken theirs down and built a wall. Mr Brown from the end of the road was staggering home from the pub holding onto the railings. We called it going home "by rail". Me and David used to sit on the railings in the summer evenings and ask anyone who looked a little drunk for a cigarette. If you were really lucky they'd give you money as well.

I lie there, in the semi-darkness, staring at me posters. I'd have to get one of this Bowie fella. Maybe I'll buy his LP. Ron in the Loft reckoned it was good.

"Tony, give it up. You're snoring again."

I could hear me Ma giving out to me Da downstairs.

"Sorry Joan, sorry."

Ten seconds later, snoring again.

I turn on the tranny. Late night summer sounds coming through.

"Starry, starry night. Paint your pallet blue and grey..."

Don McLean. That was a great song he had after Christmas. American Pie. Real sad. I didn't know what the hell it meant but Catherine told me it was the best song she had ever heard. The best song I ever heard was Ruby Tuesday from the Stones. It was one of those sinister songs with hidden meanings that always gripped your imagination.

"Well, that was Vincent from Don McLean, a song about the great artist Vincent Van Gogh who cut off his own ear."

Imagine doing that! Cutting off your ear because your mot left you?

I always put my Docs in the corner of the room. Like putting two babies to bed. Evenly together. Goodnight boots, see yis tomorrow night......

Thump, thump, thump on the bedroom door.

"C'mon Marty. Get up. It's seven o'clock"

Derek's up already watching cartoons on the BBC. I look at David's posters, half asleep. Joe Cocker. Jaysus, he's an ugly bollox.

"C'mon Marty get up."

Stagger down the stairs, quick cup of tea and I'm off. The plumber, Tony Lawlor, is waiting for me in the village outside the church. He's about thirty and a real nice guy. I see Mick coming out of the shop, paper under his arm.

"Might see yi later Marty."

Tony drives a black Morris Minor, tools all over the back seat, smell of putty heavy in the air.

"Did yi get your hole last night?" he asks.

"No, I'm a good boy" I reply.

The very thought of it. Imagine taking off your clothes with your mot and standin' looking at each other in your nip. You'd both be scarlet. Then you have to stick your mickey... Oh, no. The thought of it. Des said he did it with his girlfriend Elaine, in a field near his house. He got a French letter from a guy he works with in Jacobs. I don't believe him though.

The computer centre is nearly finished and not many tradesmen are left on the site so we do a few little jobs and it's into the hut for tea. Butter lashed on to the Vienna roll and corned beef and mustard.

A few games of cards and then it's plan time. I loved working on Saturday morning. You did fuck all and got the few extra bob in your wages and were usually home by one o'clock.

"What we'll do is drive the car up near the hut and sneak the scrap in the boot, OK?" said Tony.

Two big sacks are quickly thrown into his boot and we're off to the scrap dealer in Harold's Cross.

Tony's singing all the way.

"I'm in the money, I'm in the money"

"Oh, sorry, *"we're in the money, we're in the money""*.

Jesus, there's Billy. Billy was one of our bosses. He was about a hundred yards in front of us in the work van. Tony turns straight in the drive of a house on Rathmines Road. This old lady was cutting her grass and comes over and Tony says "Are you Mrs O'Keefe with the blocked sink?"

"No son, not me".

I'm pissing myself laughing and she's giving me dirty looks.

"Sorry missus, I must have the wrong house."

Shit, that was close.

"What the hell is he doin' around here?"

We take the back roads to the canal and drive in the back way to the scrap merchant. £18.50. Great. Tony gives me £6.50. My take-home pay is only £7 a week so it's like an extra weeks wages.

"I'll be Mickey Monk tonight" says Tony.

He lived in Drimnagh, still with his Ma and Da and his wife and two kids.

"I don't need a lift home" I said. "I'm going into town to buy a record."

I walked into town from Harold's Cross, although I hated it in me work clothes. This wasn't the real me. Clothes were everything. You judge everyone by the clothes they had on. You knew the gobshites from the cool dudes simply by their clothes. Ma said it was the same when she was young. If I heard the story about the nylon stocking after the war once I heard it a million times. They were so hard to get but me Ma had a pair!

Into a little record shop in Clanbrassil Street. I loved the smell of new records. It always reminded me of Christmas. We always got records at Christmas time. The last LP that I bought was Gilbert O'Sullivan's "Himself" at Easter. I wonder if all these songs out at the moment will still be played in twenty years time like the ones Ma and Da listen to from the fifties. I remember going into the kitchen when Nat King Cole was on the radio and seeing tears in me Ma's eyes. Probably reminded her of something. I'll probably be like that in twenty years when I hear 'Alone Again' from Gilbert of even "Starman" from David Bowie and me kids will be laughing at me.

Yes, there it was. I could see it the minute I walked in. 'Ziggy Stardust and the Spiders from Mars'. He does look a bit queer. Don't care. It's mine now. Change out of £2. I think I'll buy a single as well. Yes, I'll have 'Take me Back Home' from Slade.

"You're into queers are yi?" asked the smart arse behind the counter.

"What di yi mean?" I said.

"That song's about a fairy and David Bowie must be one dressed like that."

"He's gonna be huge, you wait and see" I said.

If I'd known he was going to be smart I would have bought elsewhere. It's like buying a brand new Morris Minor and then they're tellin' yi it's a horrible looking car. Fuck him. It was mine now. I now have ten albums. Joan and David didn't know I was buying it so they will be surprised.

No sign of the bus so I'll walk towards the city. Up past St Patrick's Cathedral, past the Ross Street flats and the Iveagh Baths. I used to go there every Saturday as a kid for a swim then straight into the shop on the corner for a lump of fruit cake we used to call 'gurr' cake. You'd be starving after your swim. Sometimes we would get off at Dolphin's Barn where there was a chipper, Mr Spud it was called, that sold you a single of chips for sixpence, then back on the bus for Walkinstown. You'd be having your swim and in the little rooms upstairs from the pool all the 'oul fellas would be having a bath or shower. Ma told us never to talk to these men as some of them were a bit 'funny' or 'not the full shillin' , as me Da would say.

"Hey pal, have yi got any odds?"

These two skinheads sitting on a window sill were giving me dirty looks.

"No, sorry" I said.

Before they could answer me there was a huge bang from up around Christchurch. They jumped off the wall and ran in the direction of the noise. I hurried myself but I was not as quick as them. Lots of people were now heading in the same direction. Across the road from the YMCA a bomb had gone off in the boot of a Garda car. It didn't look like anybody was in it but it had smashed windows, glass everywhere and wrecked the back of the cop car. Jaysus, it was real exciting. There were coppers everywhere. The street was blocked off and then the army came. Gangs of girls and fellas were all having a gawk. These skinheads started singing *"I'd like to join the IRA and furnish them with guns, throw gelignite and dynamite at all those British bums..."* like the New Seekers song "I'd like to teach the world to sing."

Wait till I tell all the gang that I'd seen this. This woman beside was shaking and couldn't light her cigarette so I lit it for her.

"My God son, imagine if you were walkin' past the car at the time. I wish they'd keep their shaggin' troubles up there."

Aw shit, now that the street was blocked off I knew I'd never get a bus. I started walking. It must be like this in Belfast all the time, I thought. After about twenty minutes of walking a van pulled up beside me and the window rolled down. It was Tony with his uncle.

"Where yi goin'?"

I jumped in and told him the whole story, adding a few bits in of course. It had blown half the street up by the time I had finished. His uncle dropped the two of us off in the village.

"Give us a look at the LP" Tony said. "Jaysus, yi must really like him, yi bought his album. I'll get a lend of it off you. What picture are you going to tonight?"

"Catherine wants to see Ryan's Daughter, it's on at the Green. I heard it's a woman's film though. We'll see."

"How much did yi get out of the scrap copper?"

"£6.50."

"Fuckin' great" he said.

I handed him a pound and told him not to tell the rest of the guys.

"What's that for?"

"Ah, you've often lent me money before Tony. Someday when I'm broke I'll get it back."

"Jaysus, thanks Marty."

We both went into O'Hagans shop and got 20 Major each and I also bought the Record song book. It had the words to most of the songs in the charts that month.

"Aw shite, I love that song" Tony said. "The First Time Ever I saw Your Face" by Roberta Flack."

"It's too bleedin' slow" I said.

Metal Guru, T Rex.

"Jaysus, I thought he was saying 'Mister Magoo, is it you?'" Tony laughed.

Then I saw it. Starman – David Bowie. I said nothing. I was so excited. There was nothing as bad as really liking a song but not knowing the words to it. For years I thought Desmond Dekker was saying "me ears are alight" instead of "The Israelites".

"Have yi heard that one yet? I said. 'Supersonic Rocket Ship" by the Kinks?". They were great when I was a kid.

"Remember Lola. That song was about a fella dressed up as a girl."

It was a great song though.

"Imagine putting on a dress and a wig and going out to a dance" said Tony. "You'd be a right sick bollox, wouldn't you."

"It's called a transvestite" I said. "They say you're born like that, some fellas actually get their mickey cut off as well."

"For fuck's sake" said Tony "how would yi do a piss?"

"Like a woman" I said "and you'd have to go to the Ladies as well."

The two of us started laughing.

Tony said "Imagine Mr Hickey next door to us turning into a woman (Mr Hickey had a big head of black curly hair and a huge beer belly). Bringing the shoppin' home with his handbag and scarf."

The thought of that vision had the two of us breaking our bollox laughing.

"And high heels and lipstick" I said.

We had both lost it at this stage.

"Well it's great to see someone happy."

Catherine and her mother. Her mother was a culchie but a nice one. She always went shopping with a trolley bag with a handle like an umbrella that you pulled along.

"How are yi Mrs Dwyer?" I asked.

Catherine had an embarrassed look on her face. We started walking home with them.

"Were you working Marty?" Mrs Dwyer asked.

"Yeah I was and on the way home I saw a car bomb in the city".

I then had to tell them the whole story. I was the hero. I was there and they weren't.

"See yi Tony".

"See yi Marty."

"Goodbye Catherine, goodbye Mrs Dwyer."

"I'll follow you home soon Ma."

Catherine stayed at the gate with me.

"What did yi buy?"

I showed her.

"Wanna come in and listen to it?"

She had only been in my house three or four times and never when me Ma or Da was there. She was still very shy.

"Naw, it's OK" she said.

"He's funny looking isn't he "she said. "Oh *Starman's* on it. He was on Top of the Pops singing it the other night."

"Shit I missed that"

"Did you get money for that scrap you were telling me about?"

"£6.50."

"You lucky swine."

I gave her a pound as well.Her face lit up.

"Thanks. I'll put that towards me holiday."

Silence. She was going to Butlins with her friends in August. Her friend Cathy didn't like me too much and knew I would hate her going to Butlins without me for a week. There would be loads of fellas there. Loads of temptation.

"Do yi want to see Ryan's Daughter tonight?"

"Yeah OK. I'll meet you at the library at half six" she said.

"Good" I said.

She wasn't allowed to go to town on Friday night yet and I suppose she didn't like me going either.

"Pity you can't go though."

There was a dance every Sunday evening in the village near the church. She was allowed to go to it. It was called the Star.

"I wish me Ma and Da were like yours" she said. "I better go. I'll see yi tonight".

I watched her walk off home. She wore black courdroy jeans, a slip on pair of shoes we called loafers, a green v-necked pullover and a Ben Sherman black and white check shirt, black hair down to the top of her bum, a big calves lick. She was lovely. I was going out with her since Christmas. She had three sisters, one older and two younger. She had just started wearing a bra. Her second favourite song was 'Let's stay together' by Al Green. Her Ma and Da were from the country and they were really nice.They had been in Dublin for years and they actually liked me. Her Da was GAA mad and went to Croke Park most Sundays in summer.

David and his friend Kieran came out the front door, draped in Afghans, jeans and clogs.

"What LP did yi buy?" Kieran said.

"Ziggy Stardust".

"Ah, Bowie. Me brother Peter has an LP called Hunky Dory by him. I'll get a lend of it for yi."

"Jaysus, thanks Kieran. Is Da in?"

"Yeah, he's watchin' wrestling."

Every Saturday, without fail, he watched the wrestling. Da actually believed the wrestling was real. He was a big child at heart and had his favourite wrestler. He'd shout and roar at the telly.

"Hit him, thump him. That's it. Now lash him out of the ring!"

He'd be doing all the actions with his arms and legs as if he was there. I couldn't wait to put on me LP. The speakers were still out on the window sill. In summer we would always sit out on the front grass and put the speakers on the window sill, volume up real loud and annoy the neighbours. Really it was just showing off.

"Ah, me arse, he didn't hold him down for three seconds, yi gobshite."

Da was losing his rag at the wrestling.

"Di yi want a cup of tea Da?"

"No thanks."

I'll have a cup of coffee, I thought, and put on Ziggy. I loved opening the new jar of coffee and breaking that new silver seal on the top. Shite, Derek is in the front room with bleeding Jungle Book again. His favourite LP.

"Derek, I'll give you 20p if yi let me use the record player."

"Yeh, OK."

No sooner had I given him the 20p than he was off like a hot snot to O'Hagans for a patsy Pop, those orange ice pops with an inch of chocolate on the top. The paper would be stuck to the ice pop so you had to blow down the side to get it off. I loved them when I was his age too. When you gave Derek 20p you would be amazed what he would come back with. Dentists Delight me Ma would call it. A brown bag with every conceivable sweet in it.

Yes, at last. Close the door, slip the LP out of it's cover. Brand new. Lovely smell. Two weeks previous we put a new needle on the record player so it shouldn't get scratched.

Starman first, then Five Years, Suffragete City, Rock n'Roll Suicide and on and on. This was bleedin' great. He was so different. Everybody had some singer or group they loved and no one else did. Tony loved Englebert Humperdink. Englebert fuckin' Humperdink. His Ma had every song he ever sang so I suppose he was so used to hearing him all the time. Mick liked The Taste. They had broken up a year or two ago but he idolized Rory Gallagher. When he left

The Taste he formed a group called Stud and we all went to see them. It was New Year's Eve 1971.

We all walked down by the canal to the National Stadium, drinking flagons of cider all the way. We were all pissed by the time we got to the concert. It was magic. We all got to the front of the stage and played our imaginary guitars and Rory gave us all the thumbs up. At half time this fella let us in to meet him and he shook all our hands and signed autographs. Tommy didn't wash his hand for 3 days. Des got so excited all he could say to him was "Jaysus, you'r bleedin' great Rory." We had met a real Rock Star. He was such a nice guy and so friendly. Tony and me begged him to play *'What's going on?'* When he did the crowd went mad. Mick reckoned it was the best night of his life ever.

Joan knocked on the door.

"Come in."

"Who's that singing?"

"David Bowie" I said, matter of factly.

"The Ziggy Stardust album?"

"Yeah. How did you know?"

"Eamon bought it last week."

Oh did he now, I thought to myself.

Eamon was her boyfriend. He was from Rathmines. They were both at university and used all these big words like "amazing" and "unbelievable". They were into the blues and had loads of albums by John Mayall.

"He has a poster of him if you want it."

"Yeah, great thanks."

'I had to phone someone so I picked on you ooo ooo. Hey that's far out so you heard it too ooo ooo. Switch on the TV we may pick him up on Channel two...'

Magic.

What did it mean? I didn't care. Channel Two, must mean BBC2. The best programme they had was the Old Grey Whistle Test with Bob Harris. Anybody new on the scene would get a slot on his show. It was different to Top of the Pops on Thursday nights. It appealed to the likes of Joan and Eamon more than me but every now and then they had someone really good on. I watched it one night and they had a group called Hawkwind singing *Silver Machine*. They were brilliant. You know when you see a group or singer just once and you just know they're great.

I played 'Starman' over and over again 'till I knew it off by heart. Then a quick sneaky look at David's LP's. I pretended I had no interest in his music but helped myself to them when he wasn't there. Yes we'll have a bit of Jethro Tull and Thick as a Brick. David's favourite song was 'Living in the Past' by Jethro and if I heard it once I heard it a million fuckin' times. Up in the bedroom I put Ziggy under the bed. I couldn't leave it with all the other records as it was too new. If someone scratched it or learned the words to the songs before I did I would go spare. The Doc's were neatly together in the corner looking at me. I lit up a Major and lay back on the bed staring at the ceiling. Life was great. The weekend was too short. The pictures tonight, chips on the way home and then a half an hour in the lane near Catherine's house for what me Ma called courting. Getting your "wear" I called it. Tomorrow, being Sunday we'd all meet in the village and decide what we will do for the day. I lay there thinking about England. I had never been there but would love to go and see all the skinheads, the clothes they wear, maybe even see a soccer match and see all the fighting. Tony had been over in April to see Liverpool play Arsenal and he was still talking about it two months later. He said he saw one gang walking to the game, most of them skinheads and suedeheads and there was at least one hundred of them. They were all singing football songs and there was a huge fight at one end of the ground. I hated soccer but I'd go for the experience. Maybe I'll ask me Ma and go over on the B&I boat with the guys.

The doorbell rang. It was Des. He had a huge bag of broken biscuits from Jacobs and gave them to me to give to me Ma.

"Jaysus, thanks Des."

"No problems" he said with a belch.

I left the biscuits under the stairs.

"I'll give them to me Ma when she comes in" I said.

Ma worked every Saturday afternoon in Crumlin and the few bob kept her car going. It was a little Fiat 850. She loved it and spent Sunday mornings cleaning it. It had an eight track tape recorder in it. I had to hide the biscuits because Derek found them once before and ate all the icing off a load of them and hid them at the bottom of the bag with all these little teeth marks all over them.

"How did it go last night?" I asked, wanting to know the juicy bits.

"I left her home to her house and I was standing outside talking to her and expecting to get me wear an' all and along came her brother. Do yi remember we got into a fight coming home from town after Christmas with that gang from Drimnagh? Well he was one of them. He gave me daggers looks and then went into the house and I could see him sneakin' a look out of the side of the curtain at me. Then a few minutes later I heard "Barbara, come in now" so after I said goodnight I was like fuckin' Speedy Gonzales all the way Home."

"So that's the end of that relationship?" I asked smiling.

"Fuckin' right" he said.

"I bought David Bowie's new album today. It's great."

"I'll have a lend of it sometime" he said.

"What are you doin' tomorrow Marty?"

"Might go into town and walk around. Maybe have a gawk in the Dandelion."

The Dandelion Market on Sunday in summer was magic. It got crammed with people, most of them with no intention of buying anything. You just went to look at everyone else. The smells and sounds in the place were great. Buskers everywhere. Even blokes selling drugs. In 1972 it was the place to be. We had all gone into the Dandelion a few Sundays ago and got into a fight. These two gobshites with Crombie coats with velvet collars kept gawking at us. Tony gawked back and one of them said "What are you looking at?" "Your ugly mush" Tony said and then it started.

Digs and kicks were issued and we sort of won. I got a thump in the jaw but kicked on of them on the leg. It was all over real quick. They just seemed to walk away and so did we. You feel great after it but still kind of shaking. Mick got two real good digs at one of them, right at the side of his face. His knuckles were red for hours after.

"We might get into another go" Des laughed. "I'm bringin' me cosh in with me this time."

Des had made us all a cosh in the workshop in Jacobs. He got pieces of rubber tube, sealed one end and filled them with sand. We all got one. One night we all walked around with our coshes in our coats thinking we were great. If the pigs had pulled us in we would have been arrested. The year before we had all got cheap leather shoes in the Iveagh Markets and put steel tips on the heels of them. We sounded liked a load of horses walking around. Me Ma hated me wearing them in the house because they marked the lino in the hall.

"OK. I'll see yi in the village in the morning."

Most Sundays we would meet outside O'Hagens around 10 o'clock in the morning and decide what to do that day and recount what happened the night before.

"Are you makin' the tea?" Da asked.

He knew bleedin' well I was makin' it but it was sort of to remind me in case I'd forgotten. Saturday evening was fry-time. Rashers, sausages, eggs, tomatoes, the lot. Seeing that I had some gosh in me pocket I said to Derek "You go back down to the chipper and get some chips and I'll do the fry. I'm buying."

His two eyes lit up because going down to the shops meant sweets again. Seven years olds have a one track mind.

"Jaysus, kid millions! Where did yi get the moola from?" Dad asked.

"Ah, a little bonus today from some scrap copper somebody gave us for nothing."

"Yi bollox yi. How much?"

"£6.50."

"No messin'."

"No messin'. I bought an LP and I'm going to save some" (me arse I am).

"That's great"Da said.

David and Alice arrived , then Joan and then Derek came back with the chips so I was run off me feet frying. They were all yappin' at the same time so I told them all to shut up. I got dirty looks all around all of a sudden.

"Shut up and I'll tell yis all what happened me today."

When I was finished telling the story of the atomic bomb going off in Dublin they all had their gobs open. I felt real smug. I was there!

The bleeding rashers and sausages were exploding as well under the grill as I check the clock.

"That'll be in the late paper probably" Da said.

Bruce and the Generation Game on the TV. Yes. I loved Saturday. The BBC had great programmes. Dad's Army. Da loved that too. One progamme I could never take to was Doctor Who. Loads of people like it but I thought it was a load of shite. Exterminate, exterminate was all they ever said. It bored me stupid. I loved the Dick Emery show and Monty Python's Flying Circus.

The kitchen was startin' to fill with smoke. The toast under the grill was burning.

"Is there something burning?" Da asked.

Is that a trick question I asked myself, with the kitchen filled with blue smoke! Trying to cook for a good few people can be a real pain. How does Ma do it? It must be even worse when we are all walking in and out of the kitchen like the animals at feeding time at the zoo. Derek never sat at the table to eat. He always lay two feet from the telly on the floor in case he would miss anything. Alice started telling us about her new job. Every Sunday in the Dandelion Market selling leather stuff. The owner was giving her £4 for working all day Sunday so she could now save for a holiday. She was planning for the following year to go to Paris. She would go and stay with a family for a month and they would send someone from their family to Dublin for a month.

The news was on the telly, showing us all the Irish athletes who were going to Munich for the Olympics in a few weeks time. They all looked like a load of gillys with their Irish uniforms.

"We'll win shag all again" said Dad. "They're all just going on a big holiday."

"I believe it's real expensive in Germany" said Alice. "A pound goes nowhere. I believe when we join the EEC next year loads of things will go up in price."

Alice was a mine of information. As long as cider and Major cigarettes don't go up I don't give a shite, I thought to myself. Everywhere in Dublin "No EEC" was daubed on walls. I didn't know what the hell that meant but I'm sure Alice did.

"Did yi hear about the Irish fencin' team that went to the Olympics?" Dad asked.

"No."

"They had to come home because they ran out of barbed wire!"

Everyone laughed, except Derek. He just gave that slight smile like he hadn't a clue what we were laughing about but it must be funny.

"Yi know" Da said "Fencin'? Barbed wire?"

"Ah yeah" said Derek. "That's stupid."

Shit. I had to meet Catherine at half past six at the library and it was six already. Upstairs for a quick wash and then into the clobber. Doc's. All shined up, two tones, red and white Ben Sherman check shirt, braces and a black blazer. I had a Leicester City FC badge Des had given me on the blazer. I knew nothing about soccer but it looked good. I wasn't shaving yet but I always put on a bit of the oul' Hi Karate after-shave lotion.

"See ya later."

Gangs of kids were playing football on the green. The tractor had been around during the week so there were little piles of grass everywhere, made into goal posts.

"Give us a cigarette Marty."

Tony's younger brother Paddy followed me up the street, dragging out of me.

"If I give you one don't tell Tony."

He was made up. I had to give him a match as well. On the way to the library I had visions of Paddy setting his house on fire.........

"And where did you get the matches son?" the policeman asks. "Marty Curran, sir. He gave me a match and a cigarette. I didn't really want it be he forced it on me. He made me smoke in the first place sir."

Little kids could be bastards. Like the time Derek found a pen in Da's car that when you turned it upside down all the women's clothes disappeared and he brought it into school and showed the nuns. We were all nearly excommunicated. Ma had to make up all kinds of excuses to the nuns. Tony told me that Paddy once put his Ma's vodka into the dogs dinner and the dog puked all over the kitchen floor and shit all over the house for three days after until Paddy owned up. Devious little bastards. I suppose I was young too.

When Ma and Da would go out on a Sunday night we used to get Ma's hair laquer and spray it from one side of the road to the other then light it when a car came along. Or knock at six doors at once and run away. One night we did that and all hid behind O'Tooles big huge hedge and when Mr Scully from down the end of the road came out, he shouted "I don't know where yis are, but I bet Curran is with yis."

I had a reputation, I'm afraid.

Catherine was there waiting for me. Pretending not to see me. She had on her dark blue gabardine coat, a check smock, white nylons and her loafer shoes. Her ma and Da let her out on Saturday night as long as her "ecker" was done. They knew she was with me, so she was "safe". Ha ha.

We headed for the bus and she told me all about her day. Her Ma thinks I'm lovely. She has good taste. Saturday night on the buses were always packed with fellas and their mots going out for the night. You'd get the bus into town and then on the bus home you'd see the same couples pissed drunk. We'll probably be like them in a few years.

We decided to go to the Green and see Ryan's Daughter. Catherine got her way! It was over 16's but at the Green you never had any problem getting in. The Green cinema had Jumbo seats for two. They were great for getting your wear in.

Bollox, there was a queue. This gobshite was walking up and down the queue playing an accordion and looking for money or cigarettes. Everyone always looked embarrassed when he got to them. One fella told him to 'fuck off' and he quickly scarpered off to the end of the queue. Well, well, well, who was on the queue as well only Patricia O'Byrne from Palmerstown with her fella. She saw me and I could see the panic in her face. So she had a boyfriend after all. Why did she fancy me then? He was a rough looking bousey. Yes. I figured it all out in my mind. She really didn't like him but couldn't tell him it was all off. Probably afraid of him. I was to be her saviour. If he found her out he would probably tear me to bits. Thanks a lot Patricia. I put my arm around Catherine just to rub it in.

There was another picture on with Ryan's Daughter. Borsalino, a gangster film. Into your Jumbo armchair, laden with goodies. A drink each, a packet of Tayto, a Star Crush ice-pop in the gold wrapping and a packet of Rolo. No teenage pimples for me! Every one of the guys had pimples. I only got one every now and then. David had loads and constantly had his mush over a bowl of boiling water with a towel over his head.

The cinema was thick with smoke. When the music started in Borsalino I recognized it immediately. The gangsters clobber was great. Most of them had pinstripe suits. I had one myself in blue with turned up trousers and a waist-coat. Every skinhead or suedehead worth his salt had a pinstripe suit. I had a Trilby hat as well with a feather in the side. To see a gang of skinheads or suedeheads all decked out in suits and Trilby hats and the sound from the steel tips on their shoes was an awesome sight. All they needed was the violin cases under their arms.

Ryan's Daughter was made in Ireland. It wasn't bad after all. Catherine loved it. Anything with love scenes in, she loved. I knew she liked it because she only kissed me once during the film. Other couples were bet into each other all through the film. You'd wonder why they even paid in at all. When Tony was in Liverpool in April he went to see a film called "A Clockwork Orange" and he said it was bleedin' great. It will probably never get into Ireland though. If it did the gobshite Censor would cut it to bits.

We decided to get the 50 bus home so walked down Grafton Street. Saturday night Grafton Street was always packed with people. On most corners someone was asking "Do you wanna score?"

£1 for an LSD tab or a small amount of hash in silver paper. Grafton Street was the best street in Dublin to buy drugs. The drug squad drove up and down a lot but didn't seem to be stopping it at all. Some guys sold sugar sweetners as acid and you ended with a turnover or a T.O. I'll never forget our experience of the drug scene.

Last year when we all left school, Tommy started working on a building site. There was an apprentice electrician there as well who had taken acid a few times and told him all about it. He said it lasted for 12 hours and it was fuckin' great. So after a meeting in Mooney's field we all decided we'd give it a go the following Saturday. We went into town on the Friday night and "Scored" off this fella outside St Stephen's Green. We bought five tabs of acid. They were on tiny pieces of blotting paper stuck to Sellotape. I remember getting the bus home that night and finding it hard to believe that I had LSD in my pocket. What if we were dragged in by the law? I knew we had done something very big.

We all took the tab at six o'clock on Saturday evening and headed off for a night out. It was October but it was a warmish night.

After about half an hour we all got the giggles. Another half an hour later it hit us all. It was unbelievable. Your whole mind and body was taken over by this tiny little piece of blotting paper. We laughed for hours at nothing. Everything you looked at was distorted and full of colours. You had this constant butterflies feeling in your stomach. You could imagine anything up in your head and see it. I got home at twelve o'clock and Ma & Da weren't home yet so I quickly got into bed. I was out of me head until about three o'clock in the morning.

When we all met the next day we had plenty to talk about. We did it about three more times up to Christmas and then Des got caught. His Da came home early with his Ma and Des was sitting upside down on the settee in his underpants, breaking his bollox laughing at nothing. He got the third degree and he gave in and told them. His Da told us all that if we took it again he'd tell the police and our parents. He was good about it though and we promised we wouldn't. It was the shock we needed. It was great at the time but really we knew it was deadly and couldn't be doing you any good. Some fellahs we knew were taking it every weekend without fail. To us they were hooked. An apprentice painter I knew from Crumlin took three tabs of acid on a building site in Clondalkin and jumped into the Canal and had to be carted off to the hospital in an ambulance. It was serious stuff.

We went into a café in Grafton Street. Two plates of chips and sausages and two Coca-Colas. I looked around at all the people in the café. It was packed. Mostly people who had been in the pubs and were all starving. Catherine played three songs on the Juke Box. *Let's Stay Together* by Al Green, *It's One of Those Nights* by the Partridge Family and *My World* by the Bee Gees. Halfway through Al Green this bloke sitting beside our table started crying. Must've reminded him of someone. Catherine went scarlet. He didn't even look drunk so it must have been serious. When it was over, I handed him a cigarette. He looked at me as if he knew I understood.

"Thanks, son. It reminds me of someone I used to know. They live in America now. It was her favourite record."

He was about thirty. I thought of Des and what he might be like if his girlfriend Elaine goes to Australia. Da told us a joke one night about two Irish fellahs goin' to America on the boat from Ireland. All the way they were telling everybody of how the streets were "paved in gold" in New York. When they got off the boat they were walking down the street and one of them spotted a $10 note on the ground. He went to pick it up but turned to his pal and said "Ah, shag it. I'll start tomorrow."

The Bee Gees were half way thru *"My World"* when half the café started singing. This big woman with a scarf said to me "Your mot's got great taste in music. I'd hang on to her" Catherine was real embarrassed... Then it was my turn to play three songs. Being real cool, I had to be different, I could see people watching me putting the money in. The trick was to sit in a café and let some other eejit spend his money on the juke box and hope they play a record you liked. *Brown Sugar* by the Stones first up, followed by *Heart of Gold* by Neil Young and *Won't get Fooled Again* by the Who. Again, most of the café joined in singing. I loved Neil Young's voice. These two clowns in Afghan coats and boots were starin' at me and me clobber.

"Had they no Reggae for yi, poxbottle!" One of them asked me. I said nothing. A voice on the other side of the café said "That's not very nice now, yi pair of fuckin' nanny goats."

Then all hell broke loose. Chairs flyin'. Salt and pepper cellars, plates and fists. Time to go. We were halfway down Grafton Street when we realised we hadn't paid. We laughed all the way to Fleet Street although Catherine was shaking a bit. "Terrible, isn't it Catherine? My mere presence can start a huge row anywhere." She laughed her head off.

Fleet Street. Packed as usual. Two women on the queue were talking about the bomb that nearly blew half of Dublin up today. Catherine looked at me and we both smiled. I was there.

Famous at last. We sat upstairs on the bus in the back seats so you could see everybody who came up the stairs. Most people were drunk. On the way home some fellah up the front let a monstrous fart and the whole upstairs of the bus started laughing except a priest who didn't look too happy. Maybe it's a sin to fart, I thought to myself.

"Are yis goin' into town tomorrow?" Catherine asked me.

"I think so. I'll see in the morning."

"I'm goin' to the Dandelion with Cathy to buy a pair of shoes. We'll meet yis there OK."

"Alright" I said.

That Cathy one will be with her, I thought. Shite.

"Why don't you buy them off Alice. She might give yi something off them."

"Ah yeah. I'll try that."

We walked thru the village as usual. Tony came out of the chip shop with a huge brown bag of chips and fish.

"How yi's goin'. Did yi go to the pictures?"

"Yeah, Ryan's Daughter. It's not bad."

"It's great" said Catherine.

"Me sister Betty's fellah is home for 2 weeks and he's loaded. He's treatin' us all to fish and chips."

Her fellah worked in the Irish Embassy in Paris and came home every few months. He had a big Citroen car and could speak French fluently. If you were in Tony's house when he was there they'd all put on real posh accents. He was to work in Paris for 5 years and then come back to Ireland for good. They had a house in Terenure but wouldn't be moving in to it until they got married. Somebody was renting it.

"I'll see yi in the morning Marty."

"See yi, Catherine."

"God. I don't know how anyone could work away like that" Catherine said.

"He's makin' loads of money though" I said. "If yi did it for a few years and maybe bought your house and had money left over it might be a good idea. Someday I'd love to go to Australia."

"Would yi?" Catherine asked.

"You can get there for £10 if you go by boat and work there for a year or two. Des was tellin' us all this because Elaine might be goin' with her family. Elaine's Da has spent the last year findin' out all about it. They'd have a swimming pool and all....."

It started to rain. There goes the courtin' I thought. We stood in her porch for a while and talked.

"Imagine wavin' from the boat to all your friends if you were going to Australia and not knowin' when you'd see them all again. That would be terrible" Catherine said.

The car was outside our house as I walked home in the drizzle. Ma & Da were in early. It was only half eleven. I walked into the back room. Ma & Da, David, Joan, Eamon and Alice were all there, giving me this funny look all of a sudden.

"What's up?" I said.

"Give us your autograph Marty" Joan said.

"What's going on?" I said again.

Ma showed me the Sunday Press. They had bought an early edition in the village on the way home from the pub. "Bomb Terror in the City" said the headlines with a picture of the cop car in bits. Under that was another picture with "Dublin shoppers look on in horror" below it. I looked at the whole front page before I copped what they were talking about. There I was as clear as day among the shoppers, me, Ziggy under me arm, looking all concerned like. I went red in the face.

"You're famous Marty" laughed me Da.

"Ah shite!" I said.

"What's wrong" asked Ma.

"It says the bomb went off at 1.06pm. We were supposed to be working until 1 o'clock in Cabinteely."

They all started laughing. I better ring Tony tomorrow and make up a story. Bollox.

"Ah don't worry about it" Ma said. "Tell them it's your twin." I sat there staring at the paper.

"You know, this picture could be in loads of papers all over the world. People in America could be looking at this tomorrow. I wonder should they pay me for bein' in the paper?"

"What picture did yi go to?" Ma asked.

"Ryan's Daughter" I said.

"It's great isn't it. Did Catherine get in OK?"

"Of course Ma. There's nothing in it. The scenery is great. All made in Ireland."

Ma said "Remember when they made the Blue Max in Ireland?" Loads of Irish people got bit parts in it. Tom & Peggy Ryan and their kids were in it and got money for doing it. They were Ma and Da's best friends. He worked in a theatre in Dublin and always got Ma & Da tickets to shows.

"What are yis watchin'?" I asked.

"The Train" Da said "with Burt Lancaster"

I made meself a cup of tea and sat in the kitchen staring at the paper. How many of me friends would see this. I'll have to buy a few papers tomorrow in case we lose this one. I read a bit of the story. A five pound bomb destroyed the Garda car.

Somebody doesn't like the pigs, I thought.

"Was it a big explosion?" Alice asked me.

"Huge" I said. "Now if yi want to ask me any more questions, talk to my lawyer."

They all laughed. I ate a huge piece of Maltana bread, chewin' gum bread we called it, lashed on the butter and watched the end of the movie. Burt Lancaster riddles the baddie with his machine gun.

"The Oak Tree pub in the village has a colour TV" Ma said.

"What's it like Ma?" I asked.

"I dunno. I'm not crazy about it. The colours all look real false. Everyone has a big red face."

"Ah I'm sure as time goes by it will get better" Da said. "We'll all have one someday."

"The reception tonight is crap" said David. "When are we goin' to get this cable thing?"

For weeks workers have been putting cables all around the roads and houses.

"It's called piped TV. It means we will get BBC, ITV and BBC2, all as clear as RTE." Said Ma.

"Not for nothing though" Da said. "We'll have to pay. Two of the bastards started fighting with each other outside Brown's the other day. I had to separate them. One of them dropped a hammer on top of the other and a mill started."

"The language out of them was like two dockers" Ma said.

"I'm leavin' Alice home Ma" David said.

"Don't be long" Da said.

"Goodnight Alice" I said. "If people start knocking early in the morning for autographs don't wake me."

"Yeah sure" Joan said.

I looked out the bathroom window. I do this every night. Why? There are so many memories on that small patch of garden out the back. A few years ago myself and Tommy made a tent and practically lived in it for all our summer holidays. We had a transistor and listened to it all day and brought in sandwiches and bottles of Taylor Keith lemonade. Our favourite song was Proud Mary by Creedence Clearwater Revival and we knew every word of it. It was our tent so we charged our friends thruppence to get in. We had candles for night time and loads of comics. Ma & Da let us sleep there some nights. We would have farting competitions. Tommy used to let on we were in Vietnam. We'd play Radio Luxembourg all the time on our little black and red tranny. Da would have to keep shouting out the back window at us to shut up. We had a flask with tea in it and a torch for when you had to have a slash.

One night a few cats started howling and fighting and we were terrified. One of the best nights in my life was in that summer. We were in the tent asleep and Da woke us up to watch the Yanks walking on the moon. Ma made chips and bread and butter and some of the neighbours came in as well. When your man walked on the moon and said "One small step for man...." I could see me Ma and Betty Ryan sort of crying. Da and Tom Ryan were a bit drunk and put pots on their heads and started walking in slow motion around the room. It was the funniest night I can ever remember. Me and Tommy laughed for hours that night. We couldn't get to sleep for ages.

And here I was only three years later, left school, drinking, smoking, girlfriend, taking drugs, staying out late. It's all happened to quick. What will I be doing in three more years. Me Airfix soldiers were still under me bed. Maybe I'm growing up too quick. I thought of all the cigarettes I'd smoked in this bathroom on the sly, waving the towel around for ten minutes after you'd had a fag. Everyone in the house smoked now except Derek. Me Ma smoked those menthol shite that tasted like peppermint. Da reckoned she was 'menthol' alright for wasting her money on them.

It was midnight and I could see loads of people coming out of the community hall in the distance. They have a dance there every Saturday night but it's crap. They leave the lights on and smell your breath on the way in. And play crap records all night. Last year I went over to the hall one night with a large hacksaw and cut off all the copper waste pipes on the outside of the toilets and kitchen and got nearly £2 in the scrap yard for them. A few days later the man who runs the hall, Mr O'Connell asked me Da would I be confident enough at the plumbing to replace the pipes as some 'little bousey' had cut them all off. No thanks! I lay in bed thinking what tomorrow might bring. Yes, I think it will be the Dandelion.

Sunday morning, millin' into tea and toast.

"Go down and get me twenty fags Marty, will yi?" Dad asked. "Silk cut."

Immediately beady eyes ran into the room.

"I'll go Da" Derek said.

"No I'll go" I said "and it'll cost Da nothing."

Derek looked disappointed.

"There's three large Taylor Keith bottles under the stairs. Yi can bring them back to O'Hagan's" I said.

Derek left the room like Speedy Gonzales. Me Ma always thought he looked so funny running down the road with the shopping bag full of bottles. He just loved having money. Three bottles gave you six pence. On the way to the shops Tommy was talking to Tony outside his house. It was Sunday morning, sunny, there were little pools of water all along the footpath from the rain the night before. I had me black brogues on with me turned up Wrangler jeans, black socks and a black shirt with a button down collar. I stepped into a puddle and the two Bolloxes started laughing.

"Fuck off" I said. "What are yis doin'?" I asked.

"We're just talking about Des" Tony said.

He met Tommy last night and told him that Elaine's oul man got accepted for Australia.

"Elaine told him they will probably be gone by the end of September. He didn't look too happy."

"That's not fair" I said. "He's been goin' with her for nearly a year. Yi can't just do that. Yi have to think of your kids. She'll be broken hearted in Australia".

Tommy and Tony looked at me, a bit embarrassed looking, but didn't say anything. They know what I meant.

"It would be sort of like a divorce" Tony said.

"Yeah" Tommy agreed.

"Shit, it's a long way away isn't it?" I said. "It's winter there now".

Catherine had an uncle who went to Melbourne nearly six years ago and nobody has heard anything from him since.

"Poor oul Des" Tony said. "He'll never watch Skippy again without cryin'."

The three of us started laughing.

"Ah stop" I said. "What are we doin' today?" I asked.

"Mick's playing a match in Mooney's field at eleven" said Tony. "Let's go and slag the bollox."

"Yeah let's" I said. "I'm getting me Da some fags. I'll see yi there."

"Des is meeting us there too" Tony said.

Bollox, no mention of me fame. They mustn't have seen the paper!

Gangs were heading down for the ten o'clock Mass. I get Mass now and then. I hated the 10 o'clock one. It was for kids and had a choir that had these makey-up songs about Jesus that all the know-alls sing along to. I preferred to go into the Church on my own and say a few prayers. When we were kids we would get into the church at a quarter to ten for a good seat.

The Mass was in Latin and the worst part was the sermon. We would spend the whole Mass staring at each other to see who was talking or messing or picking their nose or something. All the oul' ones were always dressed up to the nines and looking real holy. Some of them would try to pray and sing the loudest. You'd always watch to see who put how much on to the collection plate. Sometimes the plate would come around and there would be a big orange ten shilling note on it and you'd wonder who put it in.

"Hello Marty. Off to Mass are yi?" Catherine's mother.

"No, I'm getting it tonight Mrs Dwyer".

Mrs Dwyer was very holy and always had her prayer book and rosary beads in her hand going to Mass. Culchies were much more holy than Dubs. Into O'Hagan's for the fags. I forgot what me Da asked for but Mr O'Hagan knew. 20 Silk Cut, tipped. I had a free sneaky look through the magazines. Jackie, page three. There he was. David Bowie. Cropped blond hair, sort of orange in colour and earrings. He had make-up on and his two eyes were funny looking, like not the same. I had enough change in me pocket for it. Great.

On the way home I have a gander through the pictures. The Sweet. Yuk. Poofs. Derek loved them. Cliff Richard, even bigger fucking Yuk. On the back page Michael Jackson and the Jackson Five. I couldn't wait to get Bowie on my wall. I pushed the thumbtack so hard it bent and cut me finger. I put him on top of all the other pictures. Da looked in and stared at the pin-up of Bowie.

"Is that a man or a woman?"

"A man of course. I bought his album yesterday."

"Jaysus, I don't know... They'll be wearin' dresses next" I could hear him saying to Ma.

"Have yi seen Marty's new picture on his wall of this David Bogey fellah?"

"Bowie, Tony. He's the bees knees at the moment. He's been around for a few years but all of a sudden he's becoming real popular. He'll probably last a year like most of them."

"Jaysus, come back Buddy Holly all is forgiven, that's all I can say."

"Speaking of Buddy Holly" Ma said. "Did you know that American Pie by Don McLean was all about him and the pop music scene since he died? I heard Larry Gogan on the radio the other day talkin' about him."

Da burst into *"Bye bye Miss American Pie, Drove me Chevvy to the levy but the bleedin' levy was dry..."*

I put my new LP on again and took out the record song book. I knew Starman off by heart now. This album was brilliant.

"I got this pain in my face, this mellow thighed chick's just put my spine out of place..."

Doorbell rings. Tommy and Tony. Around to Mooney's field. Every Sunday morning one hundred George Bests played in Mooney's field. I hated soccer. I hated all the gobshites commenting from the side line. Telegraph it, the one two, he's offside, the overlap, watch the back pass. I never knew what the fuck they were on about. The referees were always bastards.

Mick played for Crumlin Wasps. He was a great player. The year before he had a trial with Bohemians Soccer Club but he was caught smoking in the dressing room with another fellah and they threw the two of them out. Mick saw the three of us and pulled a face. When I was a kid and we'd play a game on the green the two best players would pick two sides. I was always the last one left. If there was an uneven amount of kids I was left last with everyone going "you have him. No you have him" and me standing there with a big redener. It was great for my confidence. I'd stand there at the goal and wait for the ball to come up our end and them just kick it anywhere and hope it would go into the goal. All they ever said when I got the ball was "he's offside". I thought that was me footballing name they had given me!

Some bollox tripped Mick. He jumped up and pretended to head butt the fellah. The referee came over and booked him and put his name in a little book. When the referee walked away he gave him the two fingers. Des appeared.

"Hello chaps. What did we all do last night?"

"Went to the flix" I said.

"I went to the Bingo with me Ma" Tommy said.

There was silence.

"All the sixes" said Tony.

"Fuck off" said Tommy "Anyway I won £5".

"Did yi" said tony. "Yi lucky bollox."

There was a short silence as we all knew we'd never see the fiver. It was probably nailed under the floorboards by now.

"Jaysus I might go with yi next week" Tony said.

Mick hit the ball from miles out and it went into the top corner of the goal. He did a cartwheel and punched the air like the professional players on Match of the Day. Wasps were now winning 2 – 1. This man was standing beside us writing things down. Must have been a reporter from the Herald or Press. In the last minute Mick scored a penalty and the Wasps won 3 – 1.

"I have to get a drink" said Mick.

We sat on the wall outside O'Hagan's watching all the oul' fellahs going into the pub. Me Da never went to the pub on a Sunday. He preferred to go to Mass, get the paper and fall asleep watching the tele till Ma called us for our dinner.

"Did yi hear about Elaine Marty?" Des asked.

"Yeah Tony was telling me Des. I'm sorry. When will they be goin'?"

"In September" Des said. "It's fuckin' stupid. None of them really want to go except her old man. Her first cousin Peter is buying the house. I called to her house last night and her Da told me the news. I think he thought I was supposed to be delirious for him. I stood at the door with Elaine and she couldn't stop cryin'."

Des had tears in his eyes. There was a big silence. I broke the ice.

"Are we goin' to the Dandelion?"

Yes we all agreed. Meet here at 1.30.

"What's the LP like Marty?" Tony asked.

"Great. Me Da thinks he's a bum boy as well, you'll be happy to know."

"Hey listen" said Tony. "Did I hear Cassius Clay is coming to Croke Park."

"What? To play Hurlin'?" Des said.

"No yi fuckin' eejit he's goin' to box someone for charity".

"They'll need to collect some money all right for the poor bollox he'll be fightin'" said Mick.

"We should all go" I said. "He's bleedin' great. It'll be the only time we'll get to see him."

"I've never been to Croke Park" Mick said. "Me Da fuckin' hates the GAA and won't let us go near the place. He says the day they play a soccer game there is the day he'll go. The whole thing's run by corrupt bogmen, he's always sayin'".

"Corrupt Bogmen! That sounds great doesn't it?" I said.

"There was an oul' fellah standing beside me writing things down at the match, Mick" I said. "You'll probably get your name in the Herald."

"You always do if yi score" said Mick. "Me Ma keeps all the bits from the paper in a scrap book."

Loads of men were going into the pub, papers under their arms. We had all been in a pub a few times. One pub in Rathmines had a back room with a little hatch between it and the bar and we used to all sit in a corner and get someone older to order the drinks. One Saturday night before Christmas I drank three pints of Harp and then drank a naggin bottle of Vodka on the way to the Loft. I got as far as a shop doorway in Georges Street and puked me guts up all over the place. We used to put on a deep voice in the pub and Mick and Des had their Da's caps on as well. If our Ma & Da could have seen us. Like the Bash Street Kids we were.

Home for dinner. Da's watching a farming programme all about Jersey cows, all interested like.

"We're going into the Dandelion after Ma. What's time dinner?"

"One o'clock" Ma says.

Derek's playing with his Lego on the kitchen table. No one playing the record player. Great.

"Came up to you one night. I noticed the look in your eye. I saw you was on your own...." Slade, Take me Back Home. They were bleeding great. They were all skinheads once. Yes. Jethro Tull, Thick as a Brick. The cover of the album was great. Loads of reading on it. Then Gilbert.

"I've no wish to hurry you love, but have you seen the time...."

Matrimony. My favourite Gilbert song. It's funny the way you can love certain songs and other people can hate them. Everyone's different. Some people don't like music at all. There's something wrong with them. Me Granny says that you can't appreciate music unless certain songs can make you want to cry. Ma said that when they were kids, Granny would play a song called Ravels Bolero on the gramophone and she would cry. The saddest song I know is MacArthur Park by Richard Harris. I get the willy's listening to it. Dinner. Da's asleep. So much for the Jersey cows.

David and Joan appear from nowhere. Roast beef and cabbage and potatoes. Derek grabs his dinner and heads for the floor in front of the TV.

"Get back to the table Derek" says Da.

"But there's a cowboy "pitcher" on."

"It doesn't matter" says Da, with that sort of "shite, I didn't know there was a cowboy film on" look on his face.

"Have yi worked out what you're going to say to your boss tomorrow Marty, about the picture in the paper?" Ma asks.

"No. I'll have to think of somethin'. Not one of the lads said a thing to me this morning about it either."

"They probably can't read" Joan says, all university smart arse like.

Haw-haw. Real funny. With that the doorbell rang. It was Tony. Ma brought him in. He looked all flustered.

"Did yi see the paper Marty? You're on the front page!"

"I know" I said. "And at the time that was taken I should have been in the computer centre."

"Why didn't yi tell us this morning?" Tony asks.

"It's no big deal" I said, red faced.

"Sit down Tony and have some desert" Ma says handing Tony some jelly and ice-cream. The eyes nearly popped out of his head. Tony loved jelly. He would often buy a small box of Chivers jelly and eat it raw.

"Jaysus what excuse will I give tomorrow?" I said.

"Just say it's not you" Tony Says, all polite like coz he's in my house.

"Ah you'd know that mutton head a mile away" says Da and they all have a great laugh at my expense.

The phone rings. It's Tony Lawlor for me.

"I suppose you've seen the paper amigo" he says. "I've got this idea. Now listen. I lost me car keys somewhere on the job so I sent you into town to get the spare key off me missus in the Olympia." (Tony's wife worked in the Olympia box office although she wasn't there yesterday). "When you collected them you heard the bang and ran up the street. OK?"

"OK."

"Now tell us all about it" Tony asks.

I had to give him all the rundown on what happened. I felt happier now. I told them what Tony had told me to say to the boss tomorrow.

"A lie is always sinful and nothing can excuse it" Derek pipes up. "It says it in the Catechism."

Silence.

"Ah. It's not really a lie" Da says. "It's just a distortion of the facts."

"Oh" says Derek as if he understood.

Tony starts laughing. Tony loves me Da's sense of humour.

"Give us a look at the LP Marty. Jaysus he's weird lookin' isn't he. Me sister told me last night that she heard his two eyes are different because of a fight he was in. He has one pupil that stays the same size all the time."

"Jaysus that gas" I said. "I never knew that. Shit it's 1.30. Let's go."

"Thanks for the desert Mrs Curran."

"Anytime Tony" Ma says.

"See yis later".

Tony tells them all the story about the paper and me and they all want to know why I didn't tell them.

"I don't really know" I said. "I've never been famous before". A few little laughs.

"Imagine if we were walkin' around the Dandelion today" Mick said "and a fuckin' bomb went off."

"Naw, they'd never let one off there" Tommy said.

Des started laughing to himself.

"Imagine if they took a picture of yi and you were pickin' your nose or scratchin' you hole or somethin' terrible."

"Yeah" said Tony "or makin' a stupid face."

Along comes the 50. Not many people on it. The five of us across the back seat. Five pairs of Doc Martens, all Oxblood and shining. People lookin' at us as if we are going to wreck the bus.

"Did you go to your knitting class last night Marty?" Tony asks me in a real posh voice.

"No, Anthony. I was otherwise engaged" I said.

Two women with their backs to us started giggling.

"I had my bath and I washed my hair" Des said.

"And I watched the Late Late Show with Mammy and Daddy" said Tommy.

More people had got on the bus and they were all laughing.

"Michael what did you do?" I said.

"Why fellows, I drank two flagons and got fuckin' pissed."

Fits of laughter. We loved attention.

"So tell us Anthony" I said. "What form of entertainment did you partake in last night."

"Why, I did some spring cleaning in the house with my parents" said Tony and with everyone laughing Des let a monstrous belch. The conductor came flying up the stairs and warned us if we did that again we'd be off the bus.

"Ah leave them alone" a woman with her baby said. "They're only havin' fun."

"I'll decide that missus" he said.

"He needs a kick in the bollox" Mick said.

The bus stopped at the Barn and we could see a few skinheads getting on. They came upstairs and one of them said "How yi going Mick. Did yis win today?"

"Yeah, 3 – 1".

Yap Yap Yap. All looking at each other and what we were wearing. They were dog rough looking. We all got off the bus together in Dame Street. I felt uneasy with them. They were going to a shoe shop in Georges Street to look in the window at a pair of brogues one of them was saving for. We had all the gear OK but we were all basically soft as shite. We came from nice homes and families. They said good-bye and we felt relieved. Mick told us the one who spoke to him on the bus is a great soccer player and got a trial for Everton. More like a trial for shoplifting, I thought to myself. The sun was shining and we walked five abreast up Grafton Street, looking in the shop windows at ourselves all the way to the Dandelion. Grafton Street was packed and buzzing.

"Want any gear?" This bloke outside a travel agent shop asked us.

"No thanks."

"I got some great acid."

"I fuckin' said no didn't I?" Mick said.

"OK keep your hair on pal."

"Gobshite" muttered Tony.

The Dandelion was packed. All ages. All sorts of smells and sounds. Alice was in the little stall selling shoes.

"How're yis?"

She always acted differently when she met me with the lads. She lost all her poshness. All the shoes looked shite.

"Can yis not get any Doc's at all?" Mick asked Alice.

"No" said Alice "but whoever brings them into Ireland will make a fortune. There's some fellah in Sherriff Street who can get them for £10 a pair" Mick said.

"Jaysus that's twice the price you pay in England" I said.

"See yi later Alice."

Some gobshite was playing a guitar in a corner of the Dandelion, murdering "You've got a friend". We stood looking at him for a minute until Tony broke the silence.

"You've got a friend? He won't have much friends singing like that."

We started laughing and James Taylor stopped playing and threatened to shove his guitar 'where the monkey shoved his nuts' as he stared at Tony. Time to move on.

"I don't think he was too happy" Tony said.

Shit. Coming towards us was Barry Power, one of my bosses and his missus. Fuck it, I thought. Get it over with Marty. Maybe he hadn't seen the paper, I thought. He had.

"Janey Marty, I saw you in the paper."

I spun him the yarn, red-faced and stuttering. He seemed to fall for it. "Janey" was his favourite saying.

"Janey Marty, is this the way yi dress at the weekend?"

There was no answer to that. None of his bleeding business I thought to myself. A little more stupid talk and a quick goodbye. "God he's a fuckin' eejit" I informed the guys.

"Every place yi work for has one of them" said Des. "We have one in Jacobs. His name is Michael McTell. When you're talking to him he doesn't be listenin' to yi, he just keeps looking yi up and down and blinkin' all the time. I'd love to tell him he looks like a prick. When I'm older I probably will."

I felt much better now. I'll get into work a little later than usual and he will have told them all the story.

"There's a gobshite in our work as well" said Tony. "He has this stupid bleedin' laugh and he's always talking about sex. Did yi get your hole last night? Is his favourite saying. He walks around all the time holdin' a big lump of black puddin' between his legs saying' things like "Come here to me Mary, I've something for yi". One day he made a right eejit of himself. He had a pigs ear sticking out of each pocket and a white puddin' hangin' out of his fly, singing "I'm Nelly the elephant". This oul' one walked into the shop. She told him he was the most revolting man she had ever seen and was going to tell the Parish Priest about him. The boss sent some meat around to her house and apologised to her. He told the stupid bollox if he did it again he'd sack him."

Mick then told us that one of the fellahs he works with did the same thing one night in a pub when he was drunk. He pulled the inside of his two pockets out, then pulled his mickey out and made elephant noises. They all got thrown out.

There were skinheads and suedeheads everywhere. Tommy met a fellah he knew from work. His name was Billy Quinn. He had a two tone green suit on with a pair of black loafers. He looked great. He told Tommy there was going to be a row between two gangs. We decided to go over to Stephens Green for a while. The five of us lay on the grass watching the world go by. A man was sitting on a bench staring at us. Then he started all this shite "Five brave men, skinhead hardmen and their bovver boots. I suppose you're going to beat me up as well, are yis?"

Silence.

"He's a looney" Tony said. "Did yi say somethin'? Ye little fucker."

He was coming over now.

"Oh bollox" Des said.

We all looked different ways. He stood over us talking shite for a few minutes.

Mick stood up and said "we're just sittin' here doin' nothing, what are you goin' on about?"

He grabbed Mick in a headlock and then all hell broke loose. Tony smacked him in the mush with his fist. I grabbed him by the leg and pulled him to the ground. Des and Tommy put the boots in and then it was the five of us letting him have it.

"Animals, you're like animals", these two oul' grannies passing by were screaming. We scarpered out of the green and back into the Dandelion. Mick's nose was bleeding. We were all red faced and flustered looking.

"The stupid oul' bollox" Tony said.

"Let's get a drink" I said.

We went into a little café and had a big chat about the fight. Tony's knuckles were red raw.

"If the fuckin' pigs had come we would have been hauled away as if it was our fault" I said.

I didn't feel guilty at all kicking him. We were minding our own business.

"Five Coca-Colas please and five plates of chips."

Alice came into the café.

"Ah, how yis again. I saw Catherine, Marty. At least I think it was her." " A choc-ice please."

Alice had a long cheesecloth dress and you could see her knickers through it. We all pretended not to look.

"Have yi heard this song" Tony asked.

It was playing on the radio behind the counter. Rockin' Robin by Michael Jackson.

"He has a real squeaky bleedin' voice hasn't he?" Des said.

"See yis later" said Alice.

"Did yi see her knickers" said Mick.

"On her big arse" I said.

They all laughed, nervously. I think they didn't really like her but pretend they do when I'm around. She's too hippy for us. Catherine and her friend Cathy went by and saw us, then came back in.

"Were youse runnin' or somethin'?" Cathy asked.

We all still looked red-faced. She didn't like me and I wasn't exactly fond of her. Catherine sat on my knee. I think Cathy is jealous or something. She fancies Tony but he's not interested. She had to get her rub in to me about buying clothes for their holiday in Butlin's. I pretended not to care.

"I love this song" Catherine said.

Vincent was on the radio again.

"It's not as good as American Pie though" I said.

"Alice was in a minute ago" I said.

"Let's have a gawk at the shoes she sells" said Cathy.

"Naw, they're shite" said Catherine. "If we look at them we'll have to buy a pair."

"When does Elaine go to Australia?" Cathy asked Des.

Fuckin' nice one, Cathy. Everyone looking at their shoes or a spot somewhere on the wall.

"September, I think" said Des, with a sort of cry in his voice.

I'd love to give her a clatter, I thought to myself.

"Jaysus, imagine Australia. Yi can save up and go see her."

Aw for God's sake, beam me up Scottie.

"C'mon yi baldy bastard, I'll fuckin' have yi."

A row somewhere was about to start. Thank God, I thought. Des had tears in his eyes. The owner of the café ran outside to see the commotion. Mick looked at me and winked. Oh no Mick, I thought, don't? He grabbed a few bars of Cadburys chocolate and shoved them under his jumper.

Catherine ran out with fright and mouth almighty went with her. Then we all piled out. These two blokes were rolling around on the ground in a headlock. A few scrubbers were screaming "Kick him in the bollox. Reef the bastard" and things like that. A big bouncer ran in and stopped the fight.

"Yi bleedin' spoil sport" one scrubber said. A few Hari Krishnas were doing their usual Hari, Hari in a corner and one of them was bouncing around with a tambourine and came over and rubbed his hand on Mick's head and started giving him a big smile.

"There yi go Mick" I said. "He wants yi to become one. You'll look lovely in a pink dress."

Mick went scarlet.

"Who the fuck is Harry" said Tony.

"I think it's the Indian for God or something. Let's get out of here" I said.

Back down Grafton Street. The sun was shining and it had everybody looking real happy. Nobody looked happy in Ireland when it was raining. Grafton Street was full of American tourists. They stood out like nothing on earth. Check jackets, white shoes, funny hats, cameras hanging from every arm and ten times louder than everybody else. One of them came over to me.

"Excuse me Sir. Can you tell me where the Dandelion Markets are?"

"Straight up the street and it's on your right."

"Thank you, Sir."

His missus was the size of a Guinness barrel.

"I believe you were in the paper?" Cathy said. "Catherine was telling me."

I told her the story sort of pretending I was interested. I really didn't like her. She came between me and Catherine. Why couldn't she just get a boyfriend and leave us alone. Mick reckoned she was just a troublemaker. We passed the chipper myself and Catherine were in last night and the fellah inside gave me this quick stare as if he sort of recognised me. We quickly walked past and I told them all the story.

"What the hell is it with us" said Mick. "Everywhere we go we always get into a mill? I mean, yesterday somebody tried to kill Marty with a bomb!"

We all coiled up laughing outside Trinity College.

"Let's go in here and have a gawk" I said "and pretend we are all students."

There were people like Joan and Eamon everywhere with loads of books under their arms.

"Jaysus, none of us will ever get this far" said Tony.

"Bollox! Would yi like to be like these ginks?" I said.

"They all change their accents as soon as they get into university" Cathy said, looking at me from the corner of her eye. She was really slagging my sister Joan and Eamon. No wonder she hadn't got a boyfriend. Who'd fucking have her! We sat on the grass inside Trinity gawking at everyone. Des farted. Mick and Catherine went into convulsions.

"I'm not responsible for what goes on behind me back" Des said.

"You're are disgustin'" Cathy said.

"Why, have you never farted?" Des asked her.

Her face went scarlet.

"Yeah, but I do it in private" she said.

"Ah fuck that" said Des "It's no fun on your own" and he let a huge one and belched at the same time.

We were all in kinks, even Cathy.

"Do farts have lumps in them?" Des asked "Cause if not I've shit in me trousers!"

I couldn't breathe with all the laughing. There was silence then for a few minutes and we all lay on the grass staring at all the students with books tucked under their arms and yapping in little groups everywhere. Most of the girls had cords on them with Hush Puppies or sandals. Me Ma always thought I would end up going to university when I was younger. He has brains to burn, she'd say. I must have burnt them alright. Still I didn't care. I had a job and had money every week. I remember last September going down to the school for me Inter results. I was rattling. In the space of ten seconds they are handed to you and you know whether you passed or not. I scraped it with 5 'D's' and two 'B's'. I ran all the way home and when I got to our road me Ma was driving away from the house, saw me and jammed on. I jumped into the car and told her. She started hugging me and reversed back outside the house. Da was in his workshop and saw us in the kitchen and ran down to see if his offspring had any hope in life ahead of him. He was delighted and gave me a pound. It meant I could get a trade. That was the day I realised at 15 and a half years of age I could now really leave school and get some sort of a decent job. I remember buying cigarettes and cider that weekend with the pound.

Tony started singing and playing the drums on his thighs. *"Where's your Mama gone? Where's your Mama gone. Little baby Don..."* We all started singing. *"Last night I heard my Mama singin' a song..."*

"Let's get some more chips" I said.

We walked down O'Connell Street and sat in a café and gawked out the window at everyone going by. We slagged everyone.

"Look at the cut of her" Catherine said.

This huge skinhead girl went by with her fellah. She looked through the window at us and none of us opened our mouths. Her fellah had a pink pinstripe suit on with black brogues and a trilby hat. He looked magic! Where did they live I wondered? Imagine having a girlfriend who shaved her head. I imagined me Ma's face if I brought her home. 'Oh hello, Margaret, how are you, you're from the flat in the city? That must be nice and your Dad's in jail? Oh joy, and your Ma's a prostitute. Well that's different. Marty, can I have a word with you for a minute....' I started laughing to myself. The others stopped talking and looked at me.

"It was just something funny I thought of" I said.

"Tell us" Catherine said.

"No, piss off" I said.

"Tell us, yi bollox" Tony said.

"OK, I was just thinking if yi brought her home to meet your Ma & Da."

Tony started laughing.

"Me fuckin' dog would go for her immediately."

"When are yis going to Butlins?" Tony asked Catherine.

Who cares I thought to myself.

"The second week in August" mouthpiece replied. "It'll be great. There's something to do every night, and they serve yi in the pub. It's call Dan Lowrys'".

I was boiling up with anger.

"Jaysus we should have all saved up to go" Tony said.

I caught Cathy smirking over at me and I thought to myself I'll get you for this... On the way home on the bus Tommy asked me if I was still thinking about going to England for a weekend. He had an uncle in Manchester who would let us stay with him for a few days and we could go to a football match with him and do some shopping.

"That's a great idea" Cathy said. "You should go the week we're in Butlins".

That's it. I never wanted to see her again.

"Yeah, Jaysus. I'd love that" I said.

"Are yis all goin' to the Star tonight?" Tony asked.

Everyone said Yeah except Cathy. School holidays weren't until next week so she wasn't allowed out on a Sunday night. Oh, what a pity! The Star was a small dancehall that got packed on a Sunday night and it was impossible to get in smelling of drink. You had to sneak it in down your trousers or some other way. There was always a copper on the door and a few scumbags there who hassled you all night for money. Still it was somewhere to go on a Sunday night.

We all went our own ways and I walked Catherine home.

"You don't like Cathy, do Yi?" she said.

"No. I don't."

"You make it real obvious" she said.

"How?"

"The way you look at her."

"Well she doesn't like me either" I said.

"Yes she does."

Well if Catherine couldn't see it, I wasn't going to start an argument. We had a row before and it was all off for a week.

"Forget about it" I said.

Catherine's Dad drove by and gave us a beep. He'd been to Croke Park. He was from Wicklow and had a Wicklow flag hanging out of the back window. They must have won Catherine said or he wouldn't have the flag hanging out. He had played Gaelic football and hurling for his county in the 40's and every time he told me about it I had to look interested. I stood at her gate for a few minutes but she still had a face on her.

"I'll see you tonight" I said. "Outside the Star about 8 o'clock".

"OK."

She went into her house without saying anything. She was in a bad mood. Fuck. It's that bleeding Cathy's fault. Tony had three sisters and he told me that when they get their periods they are always in a bad humour. Maybe that's what was wrong with Catherine. I daren't ask her though.

Home for tea.

Derek was playing on the stairs with his soldiers. He had an Airfix plane shooting them down one by one and dropping them down the stairs. I grabbed a cushion off the chair in the hall and threw it at them and knocked them all down.

"What did you do that for?" he asked.

"That was a bomb going off' I said.

"I hate you!"

Oh great. Nobody bleeding likes me now I thought.

"What's goin' on?" Ma says.

"Nothin' Ma."

"He knocked down all my soldiers."

He was whinging now, making a big thing out of it.

"All right, shut up. I'll put them all back in their places for you."

"Will yi?"

The crying stopped now. The two of us started putting them into their places and he was in his element. I even started enjoying myself as well. It brought me back memories. When I was his age I used to bring all me soldiers out the back garden and have a huge battle in the grass and among the rockery. He was happy now. I tied his plane with a bit of string to the sweeping brush and he pretended it was flying around and swooping down on the soldiers. I felt guilty about throwing the cushion then. Ma had to have the last word.

"It's a pity you didn't do that for him in the first place, Marty."

This is turning into a bad evening, I thought.

Only Derek and me, Ma and Da had our tea. Everyone else was out. Derek horsed into the bread and jam as usual. Although I still had the dance to go to I hated Sunday evening. The weekend was over and back to work tomorrow. They will all want to know about the bomb and I'd have to get my story straight.

"Did yi keep the paper Ma?" I asked.

"Yes and I bought another in case."

"Great Ma, I'm going to put one of the pictures in a frame."

"Oh my, we're so vain" Da said.

I told Ma and Da about Des's dilemma. Da said that years ago when they got married they applied for Canada and got accepted and then changed their minds with a few weeks to go.

"Jaysus, I could have been a Canadian kid" I said.

"Are we goin' to Canada?" Derek asked, with jam all over his mush.

"No Derek, eat your tea. That's hard on Des" Ma said. "He'll be broken hearted."

"Imagine if Des and his whole family went to Australia as well" Da said "and they brought the Ford Anglia with them." Da was grinning to himself. "Can't you imagine the Ford Anglia driving around Melbourne and the whole family packed into it with the sweat drippin' off them."

We started laughing.

"With Ireland stickers all over it, and all the Australians laughin' at them."

Da was off. I could see him trying to think of other funny things.

"Pullin' into a garage and asking for 50p worth of petrol please and di yi give green shield stamps?"

Ma had tears coming down her face.

"Stop, don't be slaggin' the Irish now" she said.

"Can't yi see them broken down on a big Australian motorway and them all pushin' the Anglia, effin' and blindin' at each other. Well you wanted to come to Australia, yi gobshite."

"Yi gobshite" said Derek.

"Stop that" Ma said.

I went up to my room before getting ready to go out again and had a look through my clothes. What would I wear? My greeny-blue two tones, black laced brogues, black socks, Ben Sherman shirt and me black blazer. I lay back on the bed and stared at the poster of Bowie. What was he really like? How old is he? Is he really a queer? I must ask Ma about going to England with Tommy. If I saved for the next few weeks I could have a good few bob to spend. It'll be great though. I hope Catherine gets into good humour. I switched on me tranny and listened to Radio Luxemburg for a few minutes. The reception wasn't great but I could still make out the Chi-lites singing 'Have you seen her?' Maybe someday I'll go to Australia for a while and see what it's like. Me and Catherine could elope and not tell anyone.

The doorbell rang. It was Tony. We headed down the road as all the people were coming out of 7 o'clock Mass. Tony Johnston went by with his younger sister. He was in my class since we both started school at 4 years of age but he was a bleeding brainbox and stayed on after his Inter Cert. He nodded at me and I gave him a sort of 'I'm left school and you're not look' and 'I'm going out and having fun with money in my pocket.'

"What time are yi meetin' Catherine?"

"8 o'clock outside the Star."

We went back to Tony's house for half an hour and watched TV. His Mam was watching 'The Good Old Days' and was drinking a glass of sherry.

"How are yi Marty?" she asked.

"OK Mrs Flynn."

"Di yis want a sherry, Tony?" his Ma asked.

"Ok Ma" Tony said and winked at me.

Tony filled up two glasses with Marie Celeste sherry and we guzzled it down.

"Does you Ma and Da let yi have a drink Marty?" Mrs Flynn asked.

"Not really but I won't tell them if you don't" I said.

"Ay Jaysus, don't tell them I gave yi a sherry."

"No problem."

We headed off to the Star with smiley faces and watery eyes. Catherine was waiting outside talking to Mick and Tommy.

"How are yis?" she asked.

She looks in good humour, I thought.

"Have youse been drinkin'?" she said.

I told her about the sherry.

"Yi won't get in with that smell off yi."

Bollox. I never thought of that I said.

We took deep breaths and we went in the door.

"Tony Flynn, have you been drinkin'?" Sergeant Clarke from the police station was a bouncer and everyone called him Bilko.

"No sergeant, me and Marty have just been to seven o'clock Mass and we got Communion and wine from the chalice."

Yes, nice one Tony, I thought. He looked at the two of us and said "Go on then." We walked on, not looking back.

"I hope yi left some for the other parishioners." Clarke shouted as we went in the door.

Tony burst out laughing and we all went into hysterics inside the dance hall. The hall was only half full and the DJ was playing a slow set and nobody was dancing. We went upstairs to the shop and got a drink and crisps. Mick winked at me and Tony and lifted up his jumper and showed us a naggin of vodka sticking out of his trousers.

"Fuckin' great" Tony said.

Into the jacks and Tony poured us all one into our coca Colas. We guzzled the drinks down real quick and back into the shop. Des had arrived with Elaine and Tommy and he was talking to Catherine. The room was buzzing and all I wanted to do was dance. We sat and talked for half an hour or so. None of us knew what to say to Elaine. We daren't mention Australia. The slow set finished and we could hear 'Son of my Father' by Chickory Tip playing. We went back downstairs and stood in a circle, dancing. You could always dance better when you had a few drinks. You weren't as self-conscious.

The place was filling up real fast. Joe Nevin, a real bollox from Crumlin, walked right through us with that horrible look on his face. He was nothing but trouble. He would start a fight and always get someone to finish it for him. He hated us because we had great clothes and he hadn't. He always had a smell of him as well. Catherine hated him. You always felt uneasy when he was around. He always had these idiots hanging around with him. I swore someday I'd meet him in a dark lane with a lump of 4 by 2 and beat the shite out of him. Greyhound came on next with 'I am what I am' and we all got stuck into the skinhead dancing.

Catherine stood there going from side to side all embarrassed like. She didn't really like dancing but would always try anyway. Elaine wasn't much better.

Mick loved dancing. He bounced around like he had springs in the soles of his shoes and didn't give a shit what anyone thought. Nevin leaned against a wall staring at us. We danced for a while then sat down in the corner slagging everyone.

A slow set started and I got up and danced with Catherine. *'Jealous Guy'* by John Lennon was playing. She was in better humour again because she held me real tight and kissed me. Des was dancing beside us with Elaine. Tony looked over at me. I could see he was a bit pissed. He was humming *'Skippy'* at me and bouncing up and down like a kangaroo. Catherine saw him.

"He's a cruel fucker. I don't believe what he's doin'."

I had to hold the laugh in.

"Yeah, he's terrible isn't he?"

Then she took a fit of laughing and couldn't stop. We had to go outside and finish the laughing.

"He's so cruel" Catherine said.

"I know" I said but didn't really mean it.

We sat outside and watched the fellahs and girls still coming in.

"I was in bad humour today, I'm sorry" Catherine said.

"No, I probably wasn't very nice to Cathy I suppose."

"I wish you could come to Butlins as well."

I said nothing. Cathy had organised the whole Butlins thing earlier on in the year and hadn't included me in it. There were about eight of them going from school and no boyfriends had been invited. What if she gets off with some fellah there? Cathy will probably make sure she did. Sergeant Clarke had Nevin by the scruff of the neck and was dragging him out of the dance. He was screaming and roaring at Bilko telling him 'his big brothers would fuckin' kill him on his way home.' I was delighted and Des and Tony came out the door after them and had a good gawk as well.

"He grabbed this bird's arse as she walked past him" Tony said "and she started screaming and Bilko picked him up with one hand and dragged him out."

I love this. A dance was no good unless there was a bit of excitement. Des sat down beside Catherine. I sneaked away with Tony and left them talking. I went up to the DJ and asked him if he had anything by David Bowie.

"I don't know, I'll have a look."

I went back upstairs to the shop and Tommy and Mick were sitting watching the TV which was turned on. I got myself a drink and sat down beside them. I could see Tommy staring at my Coca Cola. There was an empty plastic cup in front of him. I sussed it all immediately. He had only brought enough money for one drink. Tough. I wasn't going to buy him one. He had as much money as me.

"Nevin got shagged out" I said.

"Yeah we saw it" Tommy said. "Did yi ask your Ma about England?"

"Nah I forgot. I'll ask her tonight."

"Manchester United are at home to Ipswich Town on the first day of the season, the second weekend in August."

That's great I thought. As long as the shops are open.

"Go and see a decent team, like Liverpool" Mick said. "Not that bleedin' poof, Georgie Best."

"Does he play for Manchester?" I said.

The two of them gave me a look. I could hear the music through all the yapping in the shop.

'Ground Control to Major Tom...' it was Bowie. I wanted to tell everyone, I know who this is and most of you don't. Catherine came into the shop. She sat on my knee and drank some of the Coca Cola.

"Jaysus, Des is real sad. He was even sayin' he might go to Australia someday himself."

"We should ring up the Australian Embassy and tell them Elaine's Da is a psycho or something" Mick said.

"He might hate it and come back after a few weeks" I said.

"No, I don't think so" Catherine said.

"It takes 6 weeks to get there on the ship anyway. They all fly out to London and then get the train to Southampton for the ship and six weeks later they get to Australia. He was telling me all this. They're going in the first week of October."

In walked Des.

"Shut up for fuck sake" Mick said.

Des sat down with us and Tommy asked him where Elaine was.

"In the jacks" he said, with a belch.

Everybody turned around and stared at him.

"Excuse me" he said real politely.

We all got the giggles and when he saw he had an audience he lifted one side of his arse up off the seat and looked at us. We all jumped up and headed for the door and he was left sitting there with a big stupid face on him. He pretended to be looking at the tele but you could see his mush getting redder and redder.

I was getting tired and I asked Catherine if we'd go early and get chips on the way home. We said goodbye to the rest of the gang and walked through the village. It was nearly dark and people were still going into the pubs. Bollox. Nevin and his shadows were standing outside the chipper.

"Give us some money Curran" he said.

I gave him twenty pence.

"You're only a poshey bollox and I bet yi haven't got your hole off her yet."

We stood in the chipper queue and said nothing. I thought all sorts of thoughts about getting the vinegar bottle and smashing it over his head but I was too scared. He was great with a gang.

"Forget about him" Catherine said.

She could see I didn't look too happy. When we were kids Da made me and David a punch bag and we hung it from a tree out the back garden. We drew a picture of Adolf Hitler on it and boxed the shite out of it. Wouldn't it be lovely to walk outside and just land one punch that would knock him out and I could walk off into the sunset with all the people clapping. We walked outside and he spat a big green snotty one in front of me. We just kept walking and

I vowed to myself that night I'd get him somehow. Chips and a spice burger. My favourite combination. We passed by Tony's house and his little brother Paddy was sitting outside the front gate with his pal having a smoke. "Give us a chip Marty", he said. I gave them a handful each and they were delighted.

"I know a joke Marty. Will I tell yi it?"

"Go on" I said.

"Why do women have diddy's?" I don't know Paddy. "So people who sell bras can have a job."

The two of them coiled up laughing.

"Can yi not do better than that Paddy?" I said.

His Ma stuck her head out the door.

"Are you there Paddy?"

"Shite" he said stamping the cigarette out real quick.

"How are yi Marty? Going home early for a kiss and cuddle?"

Catherine went scarlet.

"Yeah, see yi Mrs Flynn."

We walked past my house and the light was on in the front room. I could hear the sound of Deep Purple coming through the speakers. It had to be David and Alice. We stood in Catherine's porch talking. Her Ma and Da had gone out to friends. They went out every Sunday night to the same house where they played Irish music and sang Irish songs. How exciting! Still, they were from the country and that's what they liked. I didn't mind. I'd have a proper "court", as me ma would say, in the porch. Catherine's youngest sister, Sheila, came down the stairs and had a gawk into the porch. She was eight and was real curious about everything.

"Did yis go dancin'?"

"Go back to bed Sheila" Catherine said.

She ran into the kitchen and got herself a drink of milk. I never had a little sister, just a big one. They never had a brother. It must be a novelty to them, I suppose. We talked for half an hour and then she gave me a huge kiss and told me she really loved me. I felt great. I hated the idea of her going to Butlins in August on her own but I felt much better now. We said goodbye and

I put on my hardman walk going back to my house. Another weekend over. I started singing to myself *'No I would not give you false hope, on a strange and mournful day. When the mother and child re-u-u-nion is only a motion away....'*

Ma and Da were pulling into the car park opposite the house. I wondered if they'd cop that I had had a few drinks but I felt OK.

"Hi Marty. How's Catherine?" me Ma asked.

"Fine" I said.

"Most of our friends in the pub saw yi in the paper."

"Why di yi have those trousers up so high with those braces?" me Da asked. "You'll do yourself an injury."

"Leave him alone Tony."

Everybody was in the house. Joan and Eamon were playing chess, David and Alice were watching Monty Python's Flying Circus on TV and Derek was still up, playing with his Lego on the kitchen floor. Like a scene from the Waltons, I thought.

"Will yi get up to bed Derek, it's nearly eleven o'clock."

"Did yi not bring in any chips?" Derek asked.

"I'll give yi chips. Go on, bed."

"Marty were you in Stephen's Green today?" Joan asked.

I had to think very quickly.

"No, why?"

"A friend of mine said she saw you and some other fellahs beatin' up an old man."

"Ah, come on Joan. Who di yi think I am? We went into the Dandelion and I met Catherine."

I felt me neck going red.

"It wasn't me, I'm afraid."

"I hope not" Ma said.

Ma started making supper but I thought I'd go to bed in case I get any more tricky questions.

"Goodnight everyone. I'll make me lunch in the morning Ma."

"Yeah, and pigs will fly" Da said.

I lay on the bed listening to Larry Gogan on RTE Radio. He was playing requests for people who were phoning the station. *'Come what may'* by Vicki Leandros came on. I watched her win the Eurovision song contest earlier in the year, upstairs in the shop in the Star with Catherine. A girl from Crumlin sang for Ireland that night and we all hoped she would win.

"Well that was Vicky Leandros who sang for Greece and won the Eurovision back in April. Next up we have Johnny McEvoy with ..."

Fuck that. Let's try Luxembourg. Reception was bad tonight. I could just barely make out *'Look Who You've done'* by Slade. Shit, work tomorrow. Weekend over.

August 1972

It was Thursday evening. I had two weeks summer holidays and this was the first week. I was watching Top of the Pops and waiting for Tommy to call. Ma was driving us to the B&I boat that night. We were heading to Manchester for a few days. I was so excited. I had my small case packed nearly a week and all my money changed into English money. I had said goodbye to Catherine the night before. She told me to buy "sensible" things. I told her I'd bring her back something. She was heading for Butlins on Saturday. Tony's older sister Helena was going with her friends that week as well so I had a "spy".

Donny Osmond was singing *Puppy Love* on TV.

"What time is Tommy callin'" Ma asked.

"About 8 Ma. The boat leaves at half past ten."

"Yi have everythin' now, haven't yi?"

"Yes Ma. Black Puddin' and all."

Tommy's uncle loved black pudding but couldn't get it in Manchester. Ma had made cakes for us as well to bring and a little bottle of Irish whiskey. A group called Mott the Hoople were on next singing. *"All the young Dudes"*. Joan walked in.

"I bet yi don't know who wrote that song Marty" she said.

"Yeah I do. Big Tom and the Mainliners."

"Don't be so smart. For your information it was David Bowie."

"How di you know that?" I asked.

"It was in the New Musical Express." She said.

Good, I'm gonna buy the single in England as well I thought. The doorbell rang.

"Marty it's for you" Ma said.

It was Des. He winked at me to come outside of the porch. He stood at the front gate. He had been real quiet lately and I thought it was because of Elaine and her family going to Australia.

"How yi goin' Des? What's up?"

"I got somethin' to tell yi. I've already told Tony and Mick." Des said.

"Go on."

I was getting a bit afraid. I didn't know what was going to come out. I'd never seen him looking so serious before. There was no belching or farting or that mischievous look.

"I think Elaine's pregnant."

He looked away. He couldn't look at me straight.

"How?" I said stupidly.

"She hasn't had a period for over two months and she's been sick lately" he said.

Elaine was sixteen in November. She was nice but very quiet.

"Shit" I said not knowing what else to say. "What are yi going to do?"

"I don't know. Me Ma and Da will kill me."

Jaysus, he must have had sex with her after all. But he said he had a condom. It mustn't have worked. I was going to bring them all back condoms from England for fun. I better not now.

"C'mon over to the green" I said.

We sat across the road on the grass. I could see he was terrified.

"Did the Johnny not work?" I said, still not knowing what to say.

"We did it one night without one" he said.

I was thinking to myself how many bleeding times have they done it if that's the case. The worst I ever did was feel Catherine's diddys. But to have sex, like taking your trousers down and all... Tommy and his Da pulled up outside my house.

"Jaysus, Des, what are yi goin' to do then?"

"I don't know. They're all going to Australia in a few weeks."

This is shite I thought. I'm going to England tonight and he springs this on us all.

"Does Tommy know?"

"No, but you can tell him when I'm gone."

"Look Des, we're back on Tuesday. Let's have a talk about it then. Wait until then, don't do anything stupid. I know it must be terrible but we'll all go up to Mooney's and see if we can do anything." Do anything, I thought, like all buy him a pram. God he's in deep shit. This is going to spoil my holiday now.

Tommy and his Da were knocking at my door. They didn't see us.

"I'll see yi when yi come back Marty."

He hurried off down the road and shouted back at Tommy.

"See yi Tommy. I hope Ipswich win."

That must be who United were playing, I thought.

"How yi Tommy. Hello Mister Byrne."

"How yi Marty. Off to see the Red Devils eh? No beatin' up any skinheads now."

He came in and had a cup of tea with Ma and Da and me and Tommy watched the end of Top of the Pops. Jimmy Saville with that big cigar stuck in his gob. This weeks no 1... "He's a weird lookin' bastard isn't he?" said Tommy.

I wasn't listening. I was still thinking about Des and Elaine. Imagine if it was me and Catherine. I'd elope and not come back for years. I'd tell Tommy later I thought to myself. "I've given Tommy a few bob to give to Peter for your keep for the weekend Marty. Make sure he gives it to him won't yi."

"They'll probably spend it on the boat going over" Da said.

"Is he your brother Mr Byrne?" I asked.

"No, me first cousin Marty. He's been in England for more than twenty five years. He hasn't missed a Manchester United home game for years. Tommy tells me you don't like soccer."

"Not really."

"Even if you don't the atmosphere is great. Best, Charlton, Law and Stepney, they'll all be playin' on Saturday. Anyway I have to go. Thanks for bringin' them Mrs Curran. I'll pick them up Tuesday morning. Behave yourself Tommy."

"Bye, bye Dad."

I said all me good-byes and we were off. We drove thru the village and Des was sitting outside O'Hagan's on his own. We waved to him but he didn't see us. The poor bollox. I felt guilty going off to have fun and he's in big trouble.

"How much have you brought?" Tommy asked.

I knew the subject of money would come around. It was Tommy after all.

"I have fifty pounds exactly" I said.

"I've got forty five pounds and 35 pence."

Me Ma smiled to herself. Very important, the 35 pence I thought.

"You two be careful with your money" me Ma said.

Des's was probably sellotaped to his belly.

"Yeah Ma."

"And don't forget to bring back something for Derek for God's sake. Some sweets yi can't buy here."

"OK Ma."

Ma drove her Fiat 850 through the city and down the quay. It was Thursday evening and town was fairly packed. We drove down the Quays and the stink of the Liffey came in the window.

"Yi have your tickets?"

"Yes, Ma."

There was loads of people getting on the boat when we got there. Cars were being driven onto the ferry and there were people milling around everywhere. A coach pulled up beside us and a load of culchies got off with Liverpool Football Club scarves on them. Ma said goodbye and we went aboard. I was so excited. Will I tell Tommy now, or wait? I'll wait. We sat up on the top deck with our suitcases and gawked at everyone getting on. Tommy opened his suitcase and took out two bottles of Smithwicks. Fuckin' great.

"Where did yi get them?" I said.

"Me ol' man's stash under the stairs." He had another two in his case.

We pulled off the labels and pretended it was lemonade. We could be running away I thought or pretending we were going to England to work. We both had our Doc's on and denim jeans turned up. This man and his wife and kids were sitting near us staring at us.

"Bloody animals" his wife muttered.

Tommy heard her as well and looked at me. We haven't done anything I thought. They were judging me and Tommy by our clothes. I thought to myself what if my Da was here and heard her. He'd flatten her oul' fellah. We went for a walk around the boat. It was packed. We sat in the café and got chips and fish fingers and drank our Smithwicks. A girl on the queue was staring at us. She had jeans and baseball runners on and a tee shirt with "Slade Alive" written on it. She was about 16. She sat near us with her little sister. She asked us for the salt and started talking to us. She was from just outside Manchester and had been in Ireland for holidays. She was lovely looking.

"Are you Ok pet?" her mother shouted to her from the other end of the queue.

"Yes Mother."

They all spoke like everyone in Coronation Street. Her Mam smiled at me and Tommy and we smiled back. She told us all about where she lived and what she thought of Ireland. She told us the best places to shop in Manchester and a great dance for skinheads and suedeheads to go to. I was starting to fancy her. Her Da sat down for a few minutes and started talking to us. He told us how to get to Chorlton-cum-Hardy, the place where we would be staying. He was born in Ireland but left when he was a little boy. His name was Bill and his daughters name was Maggie but he called her pet as well. She told us she had gone to see Slade in concert in Manchester and was going to see T Rex in October. Nobody ever comes to Dublin. Maybe someday Bowie would come. I asked her if she liked him and she said he was weird. Her older brother had seen him and thought he was brilliant. The boat was leaving Dublin and we went back up on deck to look back at the lights.

"That's the first time I've ever been to Ireland. We stayed with me Auntie in Howth. Irish people curse a lot don't they?"

"Yeah I suppose they fuckin' do" I said.

She started laughing and so did Tommy. I winked at Tommy and he said he was going back down to check the two suitcases.

"Do you have a girlfriend in Dublin?" she asked.

Decisions.

"We broke up a few weeks ago" I said.

I'm a lying bastard I thought. Ah, I'll worry about it after.

"Have you a boyfriend?"

"Yeah, you" she said and laughed.

"Do you want to hold my hand?"

"Ok."

I felt this funny feeling all over me. I was cheating and only Tommy knew. She wasn't a bit shy I thought.

"How old are you?" she asked.

"Sixteen and a half."

"I'm sixteen next month," she said. "What's your favourite song?"

"*Starman* by David Bowie."

"Mine is "*Betcha by Golly Wow*" by the Stylistics."

"I've heard that one. It's a good song."

I hadn't but I wanted to say the right things.

"I was adopted when I was born" I said.

"Were you really?"

"Yeh I was. My Mam and Dad ran off to America and left me in an orphanage."

"Wow that's amazing. I wish something exciting like that had happened to me," she said.

"No. I'm only joking" I said. "I just said it to see if you would believe me."

"You can give me a kiss if you want."

I was stunned. I'd never kissed any other girl except Catherine.

"Ok."

Jaysus, she knew how to kiss. It went on for ages. I was thinking all through it that I only met her an hour ago and here I was getting me wear already. Tommy won't believe this.

"Do you like me?" she said when we finished.

"Yeah I do."

"I think your lovely" she said.

I had butterflies all over.

"All the boys I met in Dublin were horrible. Maybe you could come and meet my friends over the weekend" she said.

"I'll see" I said.

Her little sister appeared.

"Mags, Mammy wants yeh."

"I'll see yi back in the café."

"Ok."

Back down to see Tommy. He was sitting on a seat outside the café with the two cases.

"Yi bollox" he said.

"I know."

I told him the whole story.

"For fuck sake don't say anything to Catherine. Nice isn't she? Tommy, you keep your mouth shut and I'll tell yi a secret Ok."

"Ok."

When I told him the whole story about Des he felt the same as me. We'd all have to help him.

"Can't she go to England and have an operation to get rid of it."

"An abortion it's called" I said. "Catholics can't have them. It's a mortaler."

"So he really got his hole. I didn't believe him."

"Neither did I" I said. "Imagine what he's going through."

"They probably won't go to Australia now" Tommy said.

"They'll think Elaine and Des planned it."

"Hi."

She was back.

"There's a film startin' in the little cinema. Will we go and watch it? Me Mum says I can."

"Ok."

The three of us went into the cinema. *The Magnificent Seven* was showing. We all sunk into the Pullman seats and put our feet up on our cases. After a few minutes she put her head on my shoulder and held my hand. Tommy pretended not to see and looked real interested in the film. If I'd seen it once I'd seen it a million times. Every year the Christian Brothers showed it at Christmas time in the main hall as a treat for all the pupils. They had to stop it a dozen times to change the reel and the sound and picture were never together. All the kids would be shouting and talking until the shooting would start. I had to pinch myself. Is this really happening? Here I am on me way to England and this English bird is holding my hand and lying on my shoulder with Tommy on the other side. If Tommy wasn't here we'd probably be milling into each other. She's asleep. Jaysus.

"Tommy, Tommy."

"What?"

"She's asleep, for fuck sake."

I pushed her gently over the other side on to Tommy's shoulder.

"She's lovely isn't she?" I said.

"She didn't waste her time did she?" Tommy said. "Will we sleep here?"

"Ok."

We got ourselves comfortable and the two of us fell asleep. I woke up a few hours later and the movie was over and the lights were on. Tommy was hanging over the side of his chair fast asleep. Mags was gone. I wondered where. I'll go for a walk. I pushed my case under Tommy's. It was half past three in the morning. There were still people walking around. Nothing was open except a little shop selling tea and coffee. Mags' mother was buying a cup of tea.

"How are ya, chuck? Mags is asleep in our cabin. I think she likes you."

"She's a nice girl" I said.

"I bet you've got plenty of girlfriends in Dublin. Have you?"

"Not really" I said.

"Mags has a steady boyfriend in Levenshulme."

Bollox, she was lying as well. I tried to look casual. Ah well, it was good while it lasted.

"You're going to watch United tomorrow I believe?"

"Yep."

"I think they might struggle this year" she said. "They blew it last year."

I think she was looking at me for a reaction.

"Well Tommy follows them. I don't really. I'm goin' to buy clothes and things."

"Oh well don't miss the underground markets in the city centre then. See yi later."

She sounded like that oul' granny talking in Coronation Street. So, Maggie has a boyfriend after all, I thought. Ah well it was a bit of excitement. I walked into the bar and people were asleep all over the place except for a few men at a table who were singing. At least it sounded like singing. They were all pissed. *"When I first said I loved only you Maggie."* "Shut up for fuck sake."

Obviously somebody couldn't sleep. "Shut up yourself" one of them said in a big culchie accent. "Well if it isn't a bovver boy!" I've had enough of this I thought. "Yi stupid culchie bollox" I said and I quickly walked out. I heard a fit of laughing from someone in the bar. "Good on yi son."

I felt great. I went back to Tommy. He was snoring. I found a New Musical Express on a seat and had a read. On the second page there was a picture of Bowie and a little story. It said he would be soon releasing another single and would be going to America to produce an album with a fellah called Lou Reed. I felt myself getting tired again.

Liverpool at last. It was sunny outside and the boat was pulling in against the quay. We grabbed our cases and got into the queue to get off. I was starving and so was Tommy. We sat there half asleep bursting for a pee. She saw us and came over.

"Me Mum saw yi last night."

"Yeah, she did."

"Do yi want to meet me and me friends?"

Tommy looked at me and sort of smiled.

"Ok." I said.

"Right well there's a dance on Saturday night. We'll be there about 8 and it's only 50 pence to get in. Me Mum told you I have a boyfriend, didn't she? She's a real spoilsport. But I bet you have a girlfriend as well. Make sure you come coz it'll be great fun. See ya Marty. See ya Tommy."

She had written the address on a piece of paper. We got on a coach which brought us to Lime Street railway station. It was only half past seven and the next train to Manchester was at 8.25. We headed into a café. It was full of business men. We had two huge breakfasts. Then all of a sudden we were speechless. In came two skinheads. They had tattoos on their arms with LFC written on them. They both had black Doc Marten's on with faded jeans, not turned up. They had red tee shirts on with Liverpool Football Club written on the front. One of them had a scar on his neck. They were fierce looking. One of them stared at me and looked at my Doc's. He said to the other one "Fuckin' Paddy's". Jaysus, was it that obvious? We both shit ourselves.

"We're only afraid because we're in England" I said to Tommy "if we were back in Dublin we'd probably start talking to them."

They left with one of them giving us the two fingers.

"I'm bursting for a crap" Tommy said "but I'm waiting till I'm on the train in case those two killers are waiting on us."

We grabbed our cases and got tickets and got on the train. In about an hour we were in Manchester. We decided we'd go straight to Peter's house first and then go shopping. We had to walk with our cases to the bus station. There were thousands of people everywhere. It looked different to Dublin. Much cleaner. We asked a busman for directions and in about half an hour we were in Chorlton-cum-Hardy. Tommy got off the bus first and his suitcase opened and all his clothes, the cakes and the black pudding went all over the place. I felt like a fucking eejit. Another bus pulled in and drove straight over the pound of black pudding.

"Ah Bollox" Tommy said.

At least we still had the cake. We went down two streets and we were at the house. A lady was cutting the grass.

"Her name is Winnie" Tommy said to me.

"Hello there. You must be Tommy and you're Marty."

She was real friendly. She was small and fat.

"Come in and we'll put the kettle on."

We sat and talked for about an hour. Tommy told her about the black pudding and she couldn't stop laughing. She was delighted with the cake and Tommy gave her the envelope. There was a note for Peter and Winnie and an English ten pound note.

"He didn't have to do that" Winnie said "we're just glad to have you. Here don't tell Peter."

She gave us the ten pounds back. Tommy snapped it. Fuck him. I knew what would happen now. There was no way I would get my fiver. I could just hear him saying it was his dad who gave it to us etc etc.. Then a miracle happened.

"Actually hang on a minute" she said and took the ten pounds back and gave us a five pound note each. He was fuming. I could see his mush going a different colour. Ha ha! It was mine now. She told us all about how she met Peter at a dance in Leeds. They had one son who was a butcher and he worked in London. She was really nice. It was great because I was worried what sort of people they were going to be. Peter was a painter and worked for himself, she told us. He and his friend, Alan, were taking us to the game tomorrow.

We headed back into the city with all our instructions from Winnie. I couldn't resist it.

"Fuckin' great what, an extra fiver each."

"Yeah" he said, real sad looking.

We had both changed our clothes. I had my brogues on and my two tones and check shirt and Tommy just changed his jeans to his two tones as well. We got into the city and headed straight for the shops. There were Indians and Pakistanis everywhere. The clothes were bleeding brilliant. We stood there looking at all the gear with our mouths open. I bought a two tone Harrington jacket, a blue suit with parallel turned up trousers, a "Slade Alive" tee shirt, a pair of Doc Marten shoes (which I'd never even seen before) and a tartan cap and all for less than twenty pounds. When I thought of all the shite on offer in the clothes shops in Dublin, I couldn't believe this. Before Tommy bought anything he carefully added it all up in his head. He bought much the same as me but in different colours.

The shoe shop was full of Teddy Boy shoes. They called them Brothel Creepers. I don't know why. I tried on a long brown Crombie coat with a velvet collar. You couldn't get anything like this in Dublin. Tommy bought a black one. They were only five pounds each. We went into Woolworths café and stuffed ourselves. Then we bought heaps of English sweets to bring home.

"I better have that shit now before I burst" Tommy said.

When he came back he was moaning.

"Five pence to have a shite! Guess what's in the jacks?"

"I don't know" I said.

"A condom machine. They're ten pence each."

We got four each and hid them in the crombies. We had bags everywhere. It felt great. This lady was cleaning the tables.

"How's Dublin these days?"

"OK" I said. She must have heard our accents.

"I lived there up to twelve years ago."

She was like me Ma.

"We emigrated to London first but we didn't like it so we settled in Manchester."

She was originally from Finglas. Her husband was a bus driver and he was a fanatical Manchester City fan, the other Manchester Soccer club. I asked her if she thought it was better than Ireland.

"It is, I suppose, but I get terrible homesick son. Me hubby loves it here. He goes off every weekend to the soccer and both me boys play on Sunday so he's happy here. But I don't think you're ever accepted here. Anyway enjoy yourselves. I gotta get back to work."

"When we go home we can't be too happy" Tommy said.

"Why?" I asked.

"Because of Des, yi know."

"I don't know what I'd do" I said.

I imagined Catherine walking around with a big belly and me walking behind her with the newspaper under me arm going back to a flat somewhere.

"Let's have another gawk around the shops" Tommy said.

We walked around dragging all our bags behind us. Tommy spotted something in a little paper shop. It was a "Playboy" magazine. We had a little gander through the pages.

"Yi'll never see this in O'Hagans" I said.

"You shouldn't be looking at those magazines" a dark skinned fellah behind the counter told us.

"Well yi' shouldn't fuckin' leave them here" Tommy said.

We were getting real cocky now.

"Don't be so smart you. Get out of my shop."

"I wouldn't buy anything here anyway" Tommy said, getting real brave.

"C'mon, let's go" I said. "He was nice wasn't he?"

We both laughed. From the corner of my eye I saw a small little cinema with a poster of "A Clockwork Orange" on the wall.

We went over and had a look. It was over 18's. It was due to start again in 20 minutes.

"They'll never let us in" Tommy said.

"They can only tell us to piss off" I said. "Will we?"

"OK" Tommy said.

We both put our crombies on as it made us look a lot older.

"Two please" I said, in my best deep voice. This old lady with glasses stared at the two of us.

"Are you eighteen?" she asked.

"I'm nineteen and he's eighteen" me voice getting deeper.

She kept looking and then handed me the two tickets.

"A pound please."

Yes, we were in. Tommy handed me the 50 pence. Miracles never cease. Laden full of sweets and a drink we watched the movie. It was great. They were like skinheads and one of them got special treatment to try to cure him from being so violent but it didn't work. They'd never show this in Ireland, I thought.

"Bleedin' great, wasn't it?" I said to Tommy.

"Yeah."

Mick and Des will be so jealous, I thought. We made our way back to the house loaded with shopping bags. The bus was packed with people going home from work. They all sounded like Coronation Street. Peter and Winnie were standing in the garden yapping away with their neighbours. He was small and fat, like Winnie.

"You're the image of your Da" Peter said to Tommy.

He shook both our hands.

"And you must be Marty. Bought the whole of Manchester, have yis?"

He had an English/Irish sort of accent. He had spots of paint all over him. We had a yap in the kitchen and then we went to our room to have a good gawk at what we bought. We were in the back room upstairs, in bunk beds. I tried on my blue suit and Doc shoes. I made all sorts of shapes in the wardrobe mirror. We both looked great. Tommy said he thought Winnie and Peter liked like garden gnomes when we walked up the road.

We fell on to the bunks giggling.

"Tweedle Dee and Tweedle Dum" I said. That was it. I knew if we went down stairs we would start laughing.

"Ah stop" I said "they are really good for having us."

"Tommy, Marty come on down for your tea."

She had a huge tea made for us. Chips, eggs, sausages and bread. My favourite. Peter was very funny. Every time he laughed his belly jumped up and down.

"Do we need tickets for the match?" Tommy asked.

"No" Peter said "we'll go into the Stretford End you just pay in there."

"What are you doing tonight?" Winnie asked.

"I dunno" I said. "We might just watch tele."

"I go to Bingo every Friday and Peter goes to the pub with his mates. Suit yourselves, whatever you want to do."

We went for a walk after tea up to the local shops. There were a few fellahs and girls hanging around outside the chipper. They stared at us. One of the girls called us over.

"Where yis from? I've never seen you around here before."

We told them we were on holidays from Dublin. We sat in the chipper for nearly an hour talking to them. They told us that skinheads had nearly died out and long hair was going to come back into fashion soon. Jaysus, it was only starting in Ireland. They all followed Manchester United and were going in a big gang to the game the next day. One of the girls had a tattoo with M.U.F.C. OK on her arm. They had all tried acid as well and gave it up. They thought we spoke real funny. Me and Tommy felt real important. We headed back to the house.

"I'd love to live here" said Tommy. "It's great isn't it?"

"Yeah."

Winnie had gone to Bingo but Peter was still home.

"Boys, if yis want a beer there's a few in the fridge and don't tell your Mam and Dad I gave yis them."

"Thanks Peter, you're a real Dub" Tommy said.

We sat watching the TV with a Newcastle Brown Ale each and a smoke. The things you can do when you're not at home, I thought. A new mot, smokin' and drinking in the house, loads of freedom and I'm only here a day. We watched a sports programme and they were talking about the start of the football season. A man called Frank O'Farrell was talking about Manchester United and Tommy told me he was the manager. I was getting a bit excited about the game now. The doorbell rang. I went out and answered it. It was the neighbour they had been talking to earlier. Her name was Karen. She had made a big bowl of popcorn.

"This 'il keep yi goin'".

She was very nice. We were like two kings milling into the beer, cigarettes and popcorn.

"I wonder what the lads are doing?" Tommy said.

"They're not fuckin' doin' what we're doin'" I said. "Poor oul Des."

"Yeah" said Tommy.

Peter had loads of photographs in the parlour. He had a photo on the mantelpiece that just about everyone in Dublin had. Walking down O'Connell Street with your Ma and Da. Those photographers were around town all the time, especially on O'Connell Bridge and they snapped away as people passed. He had a picture of himself and Tommy's Da as kids. They looked like Biafrans. There was a picture of Winnie when she was a little girl, just as fat as she is now. There was a big picture of the two of them on their wedding day. A photo of their son behind the counter in a butcher shop was on top of the tele.

"Would yi say they're rich Tommy?" I said.

"Not real rich" Tommy said "but Winnie's an only child and her Ma and Da are dead. She was left everything. So me Da said." They always know those things in Ireland about who has what, especially money.

"Their son is after reminding me of a joke me Da told us" Tommy said.

"Tell us".

This woman goes into a butcher shop with her six kids. She was real poor looking and asks the butcher for some bones for the dog. One of the kids says "Are we getting a dog Ma?"

We both took a fit of laughing.

"My Da's favourite one" I said "is telling everyone himself and Tom Ryan when they were younger had a group with just the two of them and it was called The Symbolix. He said he was Sym and Tom was ...."

It took a few seconds but Tommy got it and started laughing again.

"It must be great when yi have your own house."

"Yi can drink and smoke all yi want" I said.

"And have sex with your missus every night" Tommy said.

"Can you imagine the two of them?" I said.

We're horrible bastards I thought.

"Humpty and Dumpty" Tommy said.

"One belling bouncing off the other" I said.

The two of us were cracking up. We heard the front door opening, the popcorn bits all over us were quickly thrown into the bowl.

"Hello boys. Everything OK?"

"Yes Winnie" we said.

"I bet Karen left in the popcorn, didn't she?"

"Yep" I said.

"I won 8 quid".

She was very excited.

"Did yi?" Tommy said. "Jaysus, remember I won 5 pound a few months ago at the Bingo in Dublin, Marty?"

Yeah I remember him telling us alright but we never saw the fiver, I thought.

"You boys must be tired?"

"I'm knackered" I said.

"Would yi like some supper?"

"Not me thanks Winnie."

"No thanks Winnie".

We went upstairs and tried on our clobber again. I couldn't wait to get back to Dublin to show off. Tommy had brought pyjamas. I couldn't fucking believe it. At the bottom of his bunk he had his Docs, turned up jeans, Harrington jacket, loads of new clothes that every skinhead or suedehead worth his salt would die for and he had brought his pyjamas.

Blue ones with white stripes.

I slept in my underpants. I wanted to laugh but I thought I better pretend I didn't notice. Peter came home from the pub. He was in the kitchen having his supper.

"Yi Ok up there boys?"

"Yeah" we said.

Tommy let a huge one rip and then I followed with a bigger one. The room smelled like the back of our work van. Every time Tommy let one so did I. It became a competition.

"I hope to fuck they don't walk in" I said "they'll die".

We heard them getting into bed. Peter farted and Winnie called him a rotten bastard. Tears were rolling down our faces. We were laughing so much we couldn't breathe. We calmed down after a few minutes. It felt funny going to sleep in another bed, in another country. I wondered what David, Joan and Derek were doing. Probably wondering what I was going to bring them back I thought.

"Boys, come on down for breakfast."

Jaysus, Winnie gets up early. Our bedroom had loads of posters of Manchester United players on the wall. It was their son's room. The posters were real old. Tommy said some of the players hadn't played for United in years. He looked so funny in his pyjamas. A lovely smell of fry came up the stairs.

"Jeesus, all they eat is bleedin' fry" Tommy said "no wonder they're so fat."

It was eight o'clock.

"Peter's gone to work but he will be back by twelve" Winnie said.

I'd never seen such a big breakfast.

"You boys tuck in. I'm going for a paper and some bread."

"We'll never bleedin' eat all this" Tommy said.

It looked like two dinners.

"Jaysus, I'm so used to just grabbin' a cup of tea in the morning" I said, although the sausages were lovely. What we didn't eat we put in a bag and shoved it down the bottom of the bin. Winnie came back with her paper and the bread.

"That was great, thanks Winnie" I said.

I was first in the loo. I hated having a crap in anyone else's house but after that breakfast I was bursting.

"What time does Peter go to the match Winnie?" I asked.

"His friend Alan is calling at one and he's drivin' you all there."

"Do yi not go yourself?" I asked.

"I've been a few times but I'm just not into it. I love watching Bestie though. He's a character. He's always in trouble. You wouldn't remember the air disaster would you?"

I didn't know what she meant. Tommy came down all cleaned up and hair washed.

"Me Da has told me about it" Tommy said.

He must have been earwigging.

"It was terrible. So many young players killed."

She told us all about it. "Albert was about eight then. I remember picking him up from school after he played a hockey game and we were standing in the chipper and the radio was on. There was a news flash that said there had been reports of an accident involving the Manchester United players. All the way home Albert kept askin' me questions. "What di yi think happened Mam?" All the way home. We had no telly then. I turned on the radio and the news kept coming in all evening. The next day we all knew how serious it was. A terrible tragedy."

She was nearly crying.

"I was at the European Cup Final though, four years ago. Peter and Albert had season tickets for Old Trafford and so did Alan and his wife. She was nine months pregnant so I was given her ticket. It was a great night. I'll never forget the atmosphere. So many people were in tears."

Over a bleeding football match, I thought to myself. Some people take it so serious.

We decided to go for a walk to the shops. Loads of people were out doing their gardens. It felt real different walking down the street listening to all the English accents. We bought more sweets in the shop beside the chipper and had another sneaky look at a magazine called Mayfair.

"Jaysus, look at the diddys on her" Tommy said. "How can we get our hands on one of those magazines to bring home?"

"I'll have to buy a hammer and chisel as well" I said.

"What for?"

"To knock a bleedin' hole in me bedroom wall to hide it from me Ma and Da."

They had posters on the wall of pop singers for 50p and there he was "David Bowie and the Spiders from Mars". He was with a few other guys in a sort of silver suit and big high laced up boots. I'll have that I thought. The girl behind the counter was real friendly and told me her granny was from Cork. We walked back with more bags and then I got the shock of my life. Tommy opened his check shirt and there stuffed down his trousers was the Mayfair magazine.

"Yi bollox yi" I said. "We could have been caught."

"Ah fuck it, 50 pence is 50 pence."

I couldn't believe it. Then we had a good gawk all the way back to the house. We sat outside on their wall looking at everyone going by. What was Catherine doing, I thought. She'd be heading off to Butlins with "bat features" by now. I missed her a bit.

"Want a cuppa cha lads?"

Winnie was at the door.

"Ok."

We sat in the kitchen after stuffing more goodies into our suitcases. Tommy hid the nudie magazine in the inside of him crombie coat. Peter came in and had these white overalls covered in paint.

"Ah yes, lads. The start of another season. I hope we don't die a death again like last year. We were top of the league last Christmas and then lost seven in a row."

I hope he's not waiting for a reaction from me, I thought.

Winnie poured his tea into a mug the size of a bleeding bucket. He asked Tommy all about his Dad and Dublin.

"I haven't been back there since 1969 but we're goin' over in October to see Colm getting married."

Colm was his younger brother.

"It's on a Saturday so I'll have to miss one game of this season."

"Oh, give over" Winnie said. "You and your bloody football."

"Eh, I heard a good one this morning on the building site. This man has a real aggressive budgie and every time he puts a mate in the cage with him the budgie kills it. The pet shop owner tells him to put a hawk in the cage with him and it will shut him up. He brings home the hawk, puts him in the cage and goes to bed. He gets up the next morning and the hawk is dead in the cage. All the budgies feathers are in the bottom of the cage and he's sitting on the perch all naked and angry lookin'. The man says out loud "What the bloody hell happened here?" And the budgie goes "I had to take me coat off to that bastard!"

Winnie went into convulsions and we all started laughing.

Peter's pal Alan walked in.

"I hope we are all this happy at twenty to five" he said.

Then Peter had to tell him the joke. We went upstairs and got ready.

"Are yi wearin' your Docs Marty?"

"Yeh fuck it lets."

Jeans, boots and my Slade Alive tee shirt. Tommy had the same but his tee shirt had a big M.U.F.C. Ok on it with the Manchester United crest.

"I hope you two don't go pickin' any fights in the Stretford End now" Alan said.

We all piled into Alan's car. It was a Vauxhall. He had furry seats and air-fresheners everywhere. Tommy had told me he was a glazier. The traffic was really busy on the way to the ground. There were hundreds of people walking and they all had red and white scarves on. We were stopped at the traffic lights and a huge gang of fellahs and girls crossed the road. They were all singing and clapping their hands. Most of them had denim jeans on and all sorts of boots. There weren't many skinheads though, mostly suede heads like us. One of them held up a big flag that said "The Mancunian Way Rules Ok".

We were getting real excited now. Tommy and Alan talked all the way about who would mark who and so on. It was like Mooneys field again. We parked in a huge car park near the canal. We could see the ground about a half mile away. Even that far away we could hear singing and chanting going on. There were crowds all packed together as we got nearer the ground. I felt a bit stupid, because I knew nothing about football. I hope nobody would ask me a question. There were people everywhere selling scarves, posters and everything to do with Manchester United and of course hot dogs.

"How are yi?"

I turned around and it was one of the girls from last night. She had a red pair of parallel trousers on and a white jumper with black runners. We told her we were with Peter and Alan and she asked them if we could go with her to the game. Peter didn't mind and we arranged to meet him at the souvenir shop at five o'clock. She was real happy looking and we went around to the back of the ground where she met about twenty other fellahs and girls.

"These are the boys I was telling yi about." They all said hello and we got on this huge queue that said "Stretford End – Juniors 40p, Adults 80p".

"Look at the fuckin' length of their hair" Tommy said.

"Yeah. I was just lookin' at that all right."

Loads of them had long hair. The girls name was Vicki.

"Are they not many skinheads around anymore?" I asked her.

"Na, long hair is startin' to come back. Boot-boys are takin' over now."

Boot-boys? What the hell are they, I thought. They all started talking to us. They were really friendly. There were huge crowds everywhere. It was so exciting. In we went. Tommy bought a load of programmes of the game. We followed them up the steps and onto the terrace. It was packed solid with young people, mostly men and boys. The ground was huge and nearly full. Tommy was beaming from ear to ear.

"Bleedin' great isn't it?"

We were all packed together, real tight. Down the other end of the ground there were a few hundred fans all in blue and white.

A few of them lifted up a big banner that said "Ipswich Town F.C." and the whole crowd at our end started singing "You're gonna get your fuckin' head kicked in". It was great. The whole football ground seemed to be singing all at once. They had all sorts of songs and clapped their hands through most of the songs. A big brass band was playing on the pitch but nobody was really listening. Then all of a sudden the two teams came out and the whole place got so loud with singing and hand clapping. The crowd called out the names and each player waved at the crowd. When they called out Georgie Best he gave a huge wave and the crowd went mad. I recognised Bobby Charlton as well.

The game started and every time United came near the goal the crowd surged forward and then backward. It was so exciting. For a second I thought of Des, in the middle all the fun we were having. He certainly wasn't having any. I felt real guilty then all I could hear all around was "Ah shit". "Ah you bloody wanker". Ipswich Town had scored a goal. The little blue crowd down the other end went mad. I didn't really understand the game but it wasn't exactly Mooney's Field. At half time the big scoreboard down the other end said "Today's attendance 56,296". Jaysus, that's more than the population of Crumlin! Vicki started talking to us and told us she lived in Moss Side.

"We're from the South Side" Tommy said and we both started laughing. We had met so many new people in the last few days. I showed her the address the girl on the boat had given us for the dance that night.

"That's bloody rough that. It's in Fallowfield. It's all reggae and skinhead music. We go to a dance near Moss Side called Sundowner. It's for over 16's. Why don't yis come tonight? It has a bar and yi can get someone over 18 to buy you a can of cider."

We looked at each other. Tommy smiled.

"We'll tell Peter and Winnie we're going to the fliks."

"Right."

The teams came out again. I had butterflies in my stomach with all the excitement. Ipswich scored again near the end of the game. The crowd got much quieter. The Ipswich fans at the other end never shut up. With a few minutes to go United scored a goal. A fellah called Denis Law kicked it into the net. Well at least I'd seen them score a goal I thought. The ref blew the whistle and the match was over 2 – 1 to Ipswich. We waited until most of the crowd had left and sat on the terrace with Vicki and her friends.

"They weren't very good were they?" she said.

"I've never been to a soccer game like this" I said. "It was bleedin' great."

"You talk like me Gran" she said.

She wrote down the address of the dance on a cigarette package. Two invites we had. I'd love to live here I thought. A lot of her friends had tartan caps like Slade. We said goodbye to them all and told them we'd be there tonight. Peter and Alan were outside the souvenir shop with big long faces.

"Rubbish, that was" Alan said. "If the rest of the bloody season's gonna be like that...."

We walked back to the car park. A coach full of Ipswich fans drove by and one of them put two fingers up on one hand and one on the other to Peter. Peter pointed to the European Cup on his scarf and held it in the air. The fellah then just gave him the two fingers again and coach drove on.

"I hope they're relegated" Peter said.

"Yeah, and probably along with us" Alan said.

Who cares, I thought. I had a great time. I was starving. I had an idea.

"Drop us off at the chipper and we'll buy the tea Peter" I said. "You'se brought us to the match."

I loved doing things like that. I could see from the corner of my eye the panic in Tommy's face.

"Yeah" Tommy said, with a bit of a cry in his voice.

"OK lads. That's very nice of yi."

Alan dropped us off at the chipper and Peter to the house. We got fish and chips and it cost £1.78. Tommy reluctantly gave me half. The miserable bollox, I thought. Winnie had given us back the tenner, put us up for nothing and he had a face on about buying the tea!

"What if Winnie has already made our tea?" he said.

"No, I heard Peter telling her he would bring in tea from the chipper."

He was going mad at this stage but he couldn't say anything.

"Let's pick out a film that we've seen and pretend we're going to it tonight."

"OK" Tommy said.

"That was very nice of you boys" Winnie said. "Yi didn't have to do that. And they were beaten were they? Ah well, there's always next week. What would yis like to do tonight?"

"We thought we would go to the flix" I said, wink, wink.

"We have a local cinema up the road" Winnie said "or you could get the bus into the city."

"Yeah maybe we'll do that" Tommy said.

They had the table already set in such a way that we could all see the tele. The Generation Game was on. They were taking it real serious. This woman was doing an impression of a bird. What a stupid eejit I thought. Imagine making a gobshite of yourself and millions of people watching you. I was thinking about Des again. What was he doing? I bet he had terrible butterflies in his stomach and probably couldn't sleep as well. I'd hate to be in his shoes when he tells his Ma and Da. Or hers, even worse and they going to Australia. They'll probably have to cancel it now. The doorbell rang. It was a friend of Peter and Winnie's. They stood at the door talking about the game and every move in it. How bleeding boring I thought. Tonight should be fun. We were getting ready in our room wondering what to wear. We didn't want to look like gobshites. Yes, denim jeans and our boots, Harrington jackets and check shirts. Can't go wrong there, I thought. Tommy wore his blazer.

"OK, this is the plan" I said.

It reminded me of sleeping in the tent when we were kids, being devious.

"We'll pick a film that finishes about half past ten or so then pretend we went for chips then home".

We had the address.

"Oh you two look very smart. You could nearly go to a dance dressed like that" Winnie said.

I nearly shit myself. Tommy gave me a sneaky look. Little did she know. We had another cup of tea with them.

"And yi met some nice teenagers at the match?" she asked.

We told Winnie all about them.

"They're from a place called Moss Side" I said.

Winnie sort of squirmed.

"They eat their young there" Peter said.

Gulp, shit, I thought. I could see it all now, flashing before me. Me and Tommy walking home in our underpants, black eyes and stab wounds, bawling crying. And Winnie standing at the door "My God did this happen to you in the cinema?" OK, option number two, I thought. The girl on the boat, Mags. Yes. I sneaked up to the room and found the bit of paper she gave us. Fallowfield. I went down and finished my tea.

Casually I said "There are some funny names in Manchester I noticed, like Fallowfield."

"That's only ten minutes from here" Peter said.

Tommy gave me a wink. He copped it immediately. He probably automatically thought to himself, yes we can walk. No busfare.

"OK, see yis later."

"OK boys. Be good now."

Off we went like two boys making their Communion.

"Moss Side me bollox" I said. "OK, let's ask someone at the bus stop."

Two women were waiting for a bus and I showed them the address.

"That's a Dublin accent isn't it?" one of them said.

They were really nice.

"I lived in Dublin during the war. We were sent over, me and two brothers because of the bombings, to live with me Dad's sister, Aunt Betty. I was just a teenager. We stayed two years and when we came back to Manchester we all had Dublin accents. We didn't see our Mam or Dad for two years. Aunt Betty let us ring home once a month. You don't know how lucky you kids have it now" she said.

Jaysus, that's an amazing story I thought.

"Anyway get this bus that's coming now and in about 5 minutes I'll tell you where to get off and it's only about ten minutes' walk after that." She said.

Great I thought. She gave us directions and we got off and started walking. I suddenly realised the busman never took our fares. Tommy looked overjoyed. We could see lots of other teenagers walking the same direction as us. Must be all going to the same dance I thought.

"You know we could nearly walk home from here" Tommy said.

How miserable I thought. We came to a load of shops and a huge hall with posters on it saying "Bingo every Tuesday and Friday. Saturday night Discoteque. Over 16's Neat Appearance".

There was a huge queue. I could smell gargle. We were getting a few stares. There were all sorts on the queue. Long hair, short hair, suede heads like us. Jaysus, last week we were lying in Mooney's getting pissed and talking about England and here we are going to a dance in Fallowfield, Manchester. The lads won't believe us. I thought of Catherine. What would she be doing now. She'd be in Butlins with "bitch features", probably getting drunk and she'd be with loads of fellahs. My mind started working overtime... In we went.

It was exactly like Dublin, ultra violet lights everywhere. We wandered around until we found the shop. Someone grabbed me by the back of my jacket. It was Mags and few of her pals. We sat down at a table and she was so excited, she couldn't stop yapping. Her three friends were Ally, Christine and Liz. Tommy had the hots for Liz. I could see immediately. *Rock & Roll* was playing. Gary Glitter. This fellah with denim dungarees and baseball boots came into the shop. He gave Mags a wink and she said come on with us. We followed them upstairs to another sort of shop where you could look down on the dance floor. There was a gang of about 25 of them. We were introduced to them all. The fellah in the dungarees had a few naggins of vodka in his pockets. Then they all produced naggins from down trousers, pockets, down their socks.

"Do yi want some money for the drink?" I said to Mags.

"No, our treat" she said.

We bought some cokes and orange and got stuck into the booze. It was great. I noticed Tommy getting really close to Liz.

"Where's your fellah?" I asked Mags.

"He's on holiday in the Isle of Man with his family."

Well.... I thought. The place was buzzin' now. Mags went to the jacks.

"She hasn't stopped talking about you since yesterday." Ally said to me. "She really fancies you. Don't tell her I told yi."

The gargle was coming from everywhere. I could see they were getting a bit rowdy. Mags came back. *"Moon River"* was playing.

"I love Greyhound" I said.

"Let's dance" Mags said.

We all went down and started dancing. The dance floor was packed. Brown Sugar came on next and they all made a big circle. One of them did a Mick Jagger impersonation in the middle.

"This is fuckin' great" Tommy said to me.

"Di yi fancy her?" I said.

"Bleedin' right."

"*I'm still waiting*" by Diana Ross came on. A slow set.

"Wanna dance" Mags said.

"Ok."

She held me real tight. Tommy was bet into Liz. Mags was kissing me on the neck. I felt all fuzzy with sort of butterflies. Then I felt a sort of pain in my neck. Bollox. She's giving me a hickey. Then we started kissing. I felt guilty. I was imagining it was Catherine I was kissing. Ah bollox, I thought, I might as well be hung for a sheep as a lamb! I felt her diddys pushing into my chest. Then I started thinking to myself, one of these friends will surely tell her fellah when he gets back from his holliers.

"When is your fellah back from the Isle of Man?" I asked her.

"Next Wednesday."

Good I thought. She was getting drunker. I knew by her eyes. They were opening and closing. We sat down again. Tommy's mot was sitting on his knee with her arms around him.

"Yi Ok Mags?" she asked.

Mags was starting to heave a bit.

"No" she said, then she staggered into the jacks.

Liz went in after her.

"I dare yi to give her a big French one when she comes back" Tommy said.

They all started laughing.

"How big is her boyfriend?" I asked one of the guys, a fellah called Bert.

"Aw, don't fuckin' mind about him. He's a prick. Yi can't go anywhere with him but he starts a fight. He's a loser. I think she's afraid of him. She's mad stayin' with him."

"Yeah, and the wanker's a City fan" another fellah said.

"Where does she live?" I asked Bert.

"Just around the corner."

"I might leave her home. I'd say she's pissed now" I said.

"Yeah, maybe we'll all go out for a while" Bert said.

A few minutes later Mags and Liz came out of the jacks. Mags was not looking too good. We all went out and had our hands stamped on the way.

"Has that girl been drinking?" this big fat lady in jeans and tee shirt was pointing at Mags.

"No missus, she's eaten some food in your bloody shop" a tall guy with us shouted back at her.

"Watch your bloody mouth lad or you won't be coming back again."

We quickly got out before she made a big thing out of it. The air hit me and I felt a bit dizzy. There was about twenty of us altogether. It was only ten o'clock. I knew in the back of my mind we had to be home by twelve. Mags was holding my hand.

"I feel a bit better now" she said.

"You should" said Liz "you left half your bloody stomach in the loo!"

"I'm starving" a fellah named Jim said. "Let's go to Bushy's."

"What's Bushy's?" I asked Mags.

"It's a Paki café just down the road. They sell great Kebabs." It was a shit hole when we got there.

"It looks a real dump" Liz said "but the food is gorgeous."

It had a juke box in the corner and we all sat around it.

"I hope I'm not going to have any trouble now children. I don't want to have to call the police again."

"No trouble, Bushy" Bert said. "We just want some grub."

We all ordered something. His whole family was working behind the counter. He has a huge amount of hair on his chest, sticking out from under his white shirt.

"Now yi see why he's called Bushy" Mags said.

Someone played *Telegram Sam* by T Rex. They all started singing. "Telegram Sam. Telegram Sam, you uuu are my main man."

Me and Tommy were smiling at each other because I suppose it reminded us of when we are all together.

"Anybody like David Bowie?" I asked.

About five or six of them immediately said yes.

"Me and me brother went to see him last month at the Apollo with his band. He's fuckin' magic" a fellah called Mark said. "He's bloody weird though. He sings in like women's clothes all through the show. The crowd loved him though."

God, this guy has seen him, I thought.

"He's gonna be really big though" Mark said.

It was my turn to stick on a song. The plates of food came.

Look casual Marty, I thought. Everyone's looking at you. Play the wrong song and you've blown your image. There was no Bowie. Three songs, 10 pence. Slade, *Look Wot you Done*. *Let your Yeah be Yeah* from the Pioneers and Run to me, the Bee Gees. A nice mixture I thought to myself.

"The chips and kebabs were lovely. I don't know anywhere in Dublin you can get kebabs" Tommy said. Slade came on.

"We all went to see them too" Mags said. "That was a great concert."

Jaysus, I thought, they get to see everyone.

"They're bloody magic" Bert said. "I've never seen any group get the crowd goin' like they did." He took out a tartan cap out of his pocket and stood up on his chair singing "Hey, Hey, Hey look wot you're doin' to me. Hey, Hey, Hey look wot you done."

"Get off my bloody chair, you hooligan." Bushy shouted.

"Paki bollox" someone said.

"Right, I'm getting the police now."

We all left in a hurry. So much for me other two songs.

"Every flippin' time we go in there we get thrown out" Liz said.

We walked back towards the dance and then sat on the wall outside. Mags was holding my hand again. We talked for ages about the way we live in Dublin and how they live here. Manchester seemed to be much more exciting. There was much more to do I thought. They all wanted to come and see Dublin though. Most of them had some sort of relation in Ireland. What's Catherine doing? Here I was with Mags, holding her hand and I was getting a bit jealous about Catherine. If only she knew. All of a sudden it was eleven o'clock. They were all going back into the dance. Mags and Liz said they'd walk back a bit with us. We ended up walking all the way back to the shops near Peter and Winnie's. They wanted to meet us again tomorrow so we decided to meet them in the centre of Manchester. We both got big hugs and kisses and we said our goodbyes. We walked home like two boys who just made their communion, all excited like.

"Tommy, how big is this thing?" I said, pointing to my neck as we stopped under a lamp post.

"Ah, yi gobshite she gave you a hickey. It's not huge but you'll have to hide it though."

I buttoned up the top button of my check shirt.

"OK, did you see Ryan's Daughter" I asked Tommy.

"Yeah it was shite" he said.

"Yeah, I saw it too. That's where we went. It is definitely on in Manchester, I saw it in the paper. What about the gargle smell?" I said.

"Aw let's hope they don't notice. If they do we'll say we bought a can each after the flix in a shop or something."

My, we're getting real brave Tommy, I thought. The key was in the door. Amazing I thought.

"They've probably left it there because they're gone to bed" Tommy said.

In we went real quiet. Winnie was fast asleep with the tele still on. We could hear Peter snoring upstairs. We stuck the kettle on and quickly stuffed our faces with bread and jam to get rid of the booze smell. Winnie woke up.

"Hello boys, did yi have a nice night?" she asked.

"Great, Winnie. We went to the flix in town and saw Ryan's Daughter and then had something to eat. It's a big city isn't it?" I said.

It all came out real quick.

"That's great" said Winnie. "Yi probably would have preferred to go dancing though. There's a good one for teenagers on a Saturday night in Fallowfield" she said.

Tommy couldn't hold in the laugh.

"Ah Jaysus Winnie, there was a drunk on the bus and yi should have heard him."

I started nervously laughing as well, trying to hold me head to one side to hide the love bite. Tommy was laughing so much snots were coming out of his nose. I thought to myself it would probably be easier if we just told her the truth.

"Some drunks can be real funny" Winnie said.

"I'm off to bed boys. Turn off the lights before yi come up. See you in the morning."

We must have laughed for at least ten minutes. I had to hold a tea-towel against my face, trying not to make noise. This was a great holiday I thought. I'm gonna save up and come again to see another game. We turned off the tele and lights and went to bed. I had a sneaky look in the bathroom mirror at my neck. Bollox. I'm in trouble now I thought. Ah I'll worry about it tomorrow. We lay there whispering for ages.

"I'd love to stay here and not go back to Ireland" I said.

"What the fuck is gonna happen to Des?" Tommy said.

"OK" I said "he's either going to just tell his Ma & Dad and Elaine's or else just run away with her."

"But they are off to Australia" Tommy said. "It's a real cock-up isn't it" Tommy said.

"I bet he can't even sleep" I said.

The moon was shining outside and it lit up the room a bit. I stared at the pictures on the wall. Brian Kidd, Manchester United. Denis Law, Manchester United. Willie Morgan, Manchester United.........

The bathroom door shut and Tommy looked over at me rubbing his eyes. We could hear Winnie banging and clattering in the kitchen making breakfast. Peter was singing in the bathroom and then he let a huge one. So did Tommy and then I did one too. The smell in the room was like a pig sty. We quickly opened the two windows and started fanning our pillows. Sunday morning. I wonder what people in Manchester do on a Sunday morning. I looked out the back window. Tommy was scratching his arse looking at himself in the mirror. He looked like something out of Sesame Street with his PJ's on.

"I wonder what's for brekkie?" he said. "Smells great."

Most of their gardens had a small greenhouse at the end. There were a few people working in the gardens already. It was just nine o'clock. Nice and sunny. I had a sneaky look at my neck in the mirror. It wasn't that bad. Catherine had never given me a love bite. Probably didn't know how. If I gave her one, her Ma would beat the shite out of her. We would be home in Dublin by Tuesday morning. It should be nearly gone by then. I put on me check shirt again and pulled it up really high. There was enough breakfast on the table to feed the whole of the Manchester United team. No wonder the two of them were so plump.

"I have to get a few presents tomorrow for my gang" I said to Tommy. "I have some sweets for Derek but that's about it."

"Go to Woolworths tomorrow in the city. You'll get everything there" Winnie said. "What di yi have planned for today."

"We might go into Manchester and look at the shop windows." Tommy said.

Peter came down.

"Morning boys. I didn't hear yis come home last night. How was the film?"

"Great" I said. "Ryan's Daughter. All made in Ireland."

"They used ordinary Irish people in some of the scenes" Tommy said. "A fellah from our work got a little part in it, Mr Hickey" he said, grinning at me.

The bollox. I nearly choked on my rasher. I looked at Tommy and he was still grinning at me. Me mush got red as a tomato. Just in time the doorbell rang. It was the popcorn lady, Karen from next door.

"Hi all."

She had a cup of tea and a cigarette in her hand. She was in for a yap.

"Did you enjoy the game boys?" she asked.

"Yeh, it was great" I said.

Tommy and Peter gave me a funny look.

"Not a great start though to the season" she said to Peter. "I think they might struggle this year. Bobby's getting on, along with Denis and a few others."

"Everything has to come to an end sometime" Peter said.

"Young McIlroy looks a good prospect for this year."

This was football talk. Even Karen knew a bit about it.

"I used to go so much in the sixties with Billy before the kids came along. Bestie, Law and Charlton. They were great years and Tony Dunne at the back. They really died a death at the end of last season didn't they?"

We left them yapping and went back up to our room. Another sneaky look at our clobber. We both counted our gosh.

"What time are we meeting them?" I said.

"One o'clock at the statue of Queen Victoria" Tommy said.

"What'll we do?"

"Ride them" Tommy said.

We were off.

"We'll turn up with our mickeys hangin' out" I said.

I loved this. We were on a roll, tears coming down our faces.

"We'll bring them to a film and sneak off when it starts."

"No" I said "Tell Liz you're sorry you kissed her because you have VD and you're really a homosexual."

"Aw, stop it will yi" Tommy said.

"And yi like wearing your sister's underwear" I added.

Snots were coming out of Tommy's nose again now. I had to stop. If Winnie or Peter came in they'd thing we were laughing at them.

"Goodbye boys" Karen said from downstairs.

"You boys look very flash. Where are you off to?" asked Winnie.

"Dunno" I said. "Probably into the city again."

"Ok. Well you have our phone number if you have any problems."

She wrote it on a piece of paper and handed it to Tommy. Peter was washing his van out the front. A blue Bedford van with a big Manchester United sticker on the back window.

"Oh I wish I was young again" he said, looking at us. "Whose hearts are yi gonna break today I wonder?"

He had a big grin. I'd swear he knew. We headed off down the road. There's something special about being on your holidays and having money in your pocket. You feel like a millionaire. We waited at the bus stop. I didn't want this holiday to end. What was Catherine doing? I bet she hasn't got a love bite on her neck like me. It's Sunday. She won't be back until next Saturday. It should be gone by then. We sat upstairs in the back seats.

"It's different to Dublin isn't it?" Tommy said. "It looks cleaner." We went past a huge park with hundreds of football pitches with games going on. I realised how big soccer must be in England and I knew nothing about the game. I was a United fan now though. We got into the city too early. It was pretty dead. Not many people around. We went into a café and got two cokes.

"What'll we do though, really?" I said.

"The fliks maybe?" Tommy said.

We sat there staring out the window.

"We're gonna have to get together to talk about Des when we get back" I said. "I'd really hate to be in his shoes."

"So he really got his hole" Tommy said. "The dirty bollox."

We sort of both laughed nervously.

"See them, they're Irish" Tommy said, pointing to a poster on the café wall. Thin Lizzy in concert.

"Your man used to be in Skid Row, yi know the black fellah, Phil somethin'."

There were all sorts of posters on the wall. Bowie was in among them. Ziggy and the Spiders on at the Manchester Apollo. Underneath was written "Coming soon, their new single, "John, I'm only Dancing". I'll have a look out for that I thought.

"There's Bowie" Tommy said, pointing at the poster. "Imagine if he was playin' here tonight. You'd be able to go and see him. It was great seeing a Clockwork Orange though" he said. "We should buy two bowler hats and walkin' sticks like your man had and start a new trend when we get back."

When we get back I thought. Back to work in a week, shite. I was having such a great time. Freedom. I was missing Catherine a little bit. I was picturing in my mind some bollox giving her a love bite. I was getting jealous.

"Let's go" Tommy said.

It was five to one. We walked down to Piccadilly Square. The two girls were sitting at the statue of Queen Victoria. Both of them had bib & brace denim overalls on with round necked tee-shirts. Mags had on a pair of black Doc Marten shoes and Liz had a white pair of bumper boots.

"How yi goin'?" Tommy said.

"We got here at twelve" Liz said. "We couldn't remember if we said twelve or one."

Mags immediately held my hand. Jaysus she's real serious, I thought. We sat talking for a few minutes then Mags said "Let's go to Stockport for something to do."

"Ok" we said.

Where the hell is Stockport I thought. We walked to a bus station and sat waiting for the bus. Mags smelled lovely. She had makeup on and lipstick. She looked much older. We got on the bus and went upstairs. It was like a Dublin bus. There were things written all over the backs of the seats and windows. County Rule Ok, Stockport Rule Ok. Stockport must have a football team. We sat at the back as usual and lit up our fags.

"Were you smokin' last night?" Mags asked me.

"Yeah" I said.

"I can't remember" she said.

"No wonder" Liz said. "You had a skinful. Have yi ever smoked dope?" Liz asked us.

"Yeah" I said, real cocky like.

She opened the top zip pocket of her overalls and showed us a huge joint.

"Where the bloody hell did you get that?" Mags asked.

"Mind your own business."

Tommy gave me a look. I had that funny sort of butterfly feeling in my stomach again. Here I was on a bus going to God knows where with two mots and a big fucking joint. What if we were caught... "Hello Mam, Marty here. I'm staying in Manchester a little bit longer than planned, like 10 years."

After about half an hour or so we got to Stockport. Mags was still holding my hand real tight. We walked around for a while and ended up in a park with a little lake. The joint came out. We all had a few puffs. I didn't really want to but I thought I'll look like a sap if I didn't. There was a little shop in the park and Tommy and I decided to get some cokes. We were feeling a bit giddy now after the few drags on the joint. Tommy started laughing at nothing. Then I got the fright of my bleeding life. "Jesus Tommy look" I said.

A copper with one of those funny hats had a hold of Mags by the arm and another one had Liz up against a bush searching her. He had the joint in his hand and was talking to someone on a walkie-talkie. We were about 100 yards away. Liz looked at us straight in the eye and she shook her head from side to side slowly. We got the hint immediately. We walked off quickly in the opposite direction, shitting ourselves.

"Holy fuckin' bollox" Tommy said. "Di yi think they'll say we were with them? I never saw them comin' from anywhere did you?"

My hands were shaking. We walked for miles until we came to a bus stop.

"Jaysus, that's all we need" I said.

"Ok, let's be calm. If they don't say anything we have nothing to be worried about" Tommy said.

"I really don't think they will" I said.

A bus came with Manchester Piccadilly on it. We sat at the back staring out the window. I could see Tommy was still a bit giddy looking. He started laughing again.

"It's not fuckin' funny" I said.

But I started laughing as well. It was sort of a nervous laugh. All sorts of things were going thru my mind. The evening news "Do you recognise these boys, Irish accents, very obvious new clothes, called Marty and Tommy."

I had butterflies again. We got back into the city. We sat in the bus depot thinking.

"There's only one thing to do" I said. "We'll go back to Fallowfield tonight, see if we recognize anyone from last night and find out what happened to them. They'll probably be charged and then let go home."

What if their friends think we scarpered and beat the shite out of us, I thought. It was getting near tea-time so we decided to go back to Peter and Winnie's.

"We'll tell them we got a bus to Stockport for something to do." I said.

"Ok".

My stomach was sick. We had so much fun since we left Dublin on Thursday night and now this happens. I thought of Catherine. What would she think? The two of us caught smoking a joint in a park in England with two mots. Her Ma would never let me in the house again. Peter was doing his garden. We stood there trying to make conversation but we only wanted to go up to our room. Winnie had gone out to a friends' house and had made a load of sandwiches and cakes and left them on the kitchen table for us. We barely ate anything. I just wanted to go to Fallowfield and see what the story was. So did Tommy. It was like being in court and waiting to see if you are guilty or innocent. We sat watching tele for a while.

"You're very quiet tonight boys" Peter said.

"Ah, we saw a lady getting knocked off her bike on the way home. It gives yi a bit of a fright" Tommy said.

Where the fuck does he get them, I thought. Tommy Christian Andersen. Then he proceeded to tell a huge story about this old lady and they had to sit her at the side of the road and someone gave her a cup of tea and so on. I was laughing so much inside but I couldn't show it. I left him yapping with Peter and went upstairs. I sat on the bed sort of laughing and crying at the same time. A few minutes later Tommy came up and we both cracked up.

"Jaysus, I don't know how yi keep a straight face" I said.

"I never have any problem lyin'" Tommy said. "Ok, let's face the fuckin' music" he said.

I was seeing a different Tommy than the one we all knew. I suppose you don't know somebody until you live with them for a little while. That's what me Ma always said. He was funnier than I thought. He'll probably always be mean though, you can't change that.

We told Peter we were going to get a few buses around Manchester and have a look before we go home tomorrow.

"Avoid Moss Side" Peter said.

Jaysus, it must be bad I thought.

"See yi later boys and be careful."

We headed off not saying much. I was nervously singing Bowie to myself. *"Hey man, I got this pain in my face, this mellow thighed chick's just put my spine out of place"*. To hell with it I thought. If the police grabbed us we'd just tell the truth. We didn't ask them to bring the shit. I was feeling a bit braver now. We got on the bus, still not saying much, staring out the window. If my Ma and Da knew some of the things we get up to. "They're off to Manchester for a little bit of shopping and to see Georgie playing soccer" I heard her tell one of the neighbours. We're little bollox's at times, I thought. The hardship we put them through.

We arrived at Fallowfield. We still hadn't said a word to each other. I wished I was back in Dublin. I'll just get back on the next bus and go back to Peters', grab my case and go home. Why were we doing this? We're gobshites I thought. There weren't many people about. We walked past the dancehall and then on to Bushy's café.

"There's nobody around" Tommy said.

Then we heard someone calling us. It was Mags. She was on the other side of the road with two other girls we hadn't seen before. She didn't look too angry. We both said nothing. The two girls walked on and she crossed the road. All of a sudden she started crying and apologising to us. They could have got us into trouble and so on. Tommy looked at me and we both felt a huge weight gone off our shoulders all of a sudden.

"Come into the café" I said.

We sat down and ordered three cokes. I paid. I knew I'd have to. Mags said it wasn't fair as we didn't know about the joint and the police didn't arrest them or anything but took their names and searched them and told them their parents would be informed and all that shit. All our worry was for nothing, I thought.

"We didn't think we'd ever see you again" she said.

She seemed delighted we came.

"Where's Liz?" Tommy asked.

"She told her Mum. She said she couldn't just wait for the police to call she'd rather just get it over and done with. She won't be allowed out for a whole month."

Tommy looked a bit disappointed. I didn't. I felt so relieved. I just wanted to give Mags a huge kiss.

"Is there a dance tonight?" I asked.

"No" said Mags "only on Saturday nights."

She looked really happy all of a sudden.

"I'm starving" I said.

My appetite had suddenly come back.

"Let's go into the city" Mags said.

She had on a black Harrington on with a denim skirt and a pair of loafers and a tee-shirt with the Osmonds on it. I had a great idea. I'll buy Catherine a Harrington jacket and a Slade tee-shirt. We got on the bus and headed for the centre of Manchester. Catherine wouldn't be allowed to go into town like that. She'd have to ask her Ma and Da and tell them all the time where she was going and who with. Maybe Mags is a bit wild I thought. I don't care.

We went into a Wimpy café and horsed into the food. We had Wimpy burgers and chips, cokes and three huge Knickerbocker Glorys. Tommy and I split the bill and he didn't seem to mind handing out the cash. We couldn't let Mags pay. I think we were both on a high. I really had visions of us getting the shite beaten out of us. Mags was holding my hand again. We sat there talking about Ireland and our gang and how she's have to come over and see us all someday. We told her about Des and the predicament he was in. She said a girl in her school got pregnant and had an abortion but she had gone a little bit screwy and had to now go to a psychiatrist from time to time. Her Ma and Da made her get rid of the baby. She was only 16. The fellah who was the baby's father went to live in London. Mags told us all about London. She had been a few times with all the United fans and loved it. "It's bloody huge" she said. "We went to see the Reds play Spurs and we were all in one end of the ground and the Spurs fans pelted us with coins and stones. They hate us when we come to town. I'm going with me brother to Anfield on Tuesday. We play the scouse bastards."

What the hell was she talking about?

"What's a scouse?" I asked.

"Liverpool, it's their nickname. Scousers. They play in Anfield" Tommy said.

"Oh I see" I said, trying to look interested. Mags was writing on my arm with a biro. The Mancunian Way Rules Ok! I felt great. It was like a tattoo. She had now given me a hickey and a tattoo. She wrote down her address and Liz's and we gave her ours. We walked around the city for a while but it was getting late. We got back to Fallowfield about half past nine and we sat on a wall near her house. It was funny because I knew I would probably never see her again but it was exciting having another girlfriend for a few days. Maybe Catherine is with another fellah. I was getting jealous again. We talked for about half an hour then Tommy did something really nice. I'll be at the bus stop Marty.

"See yi Mags, nice knowin' yi. I hope United win the league this year."

She gave him a hug and he went off giving me a wink.

"He's lovely isn't he" Mags said. "It's a pity Liz couldn't be here."

We talked for a few minutes then got into the serious business of kissing. She went to give me another love bit but I stopped her. "Don't Mags I'm probably in enough trouble already" I said. She just laughed. I had visions of Tommy on his own at the bus stop getting his head kicked in. We said our goodbyes and Mags had a few tears in her eyes.

"Si yi chuck".

She walked off wiping her eyes in her Harrington. I was a bit sad myself. We could have arranged to meet the next day but I knew we wouldn't have the time. Tommy was sitting in the bus shelter having a smoke. We both sat there and had a fag. "Ah fuck it, I thought it was going to be a poxy night" Tommy said. "It's a pity Liz couldn't be there" I said.

"Ah who gives a bollox" he said.

The bus came. We sat upstairs in the back seat. Tommy started singing to himself. There was nobody else on the bus. *"Well if you've got a wingo, take her up to Ringo, where the waxies singo all the day. If you've had your fill of porter and yi can't go any further, give her man the order, back to the quay"*. The two of us were singing now *"and take her up to Monto, Monto..."* An old lady with a scarf and her hair in curlers came upstairs.

"You boys are very happy tonight" she said.

"Yes Missus" Tommy said "we won at the bingo."

She didn't find us funny. Lucky our stop was next. We walked back to Peter and Winnie's, singing all the way. *"I'll tell me Ma when I go home, the boys won't leave the girls alone, they pull their hair, they stole their combs..."* We were happy again.

We sat talking to Peter and Winnie for a while. We were leaving the next day so we wouldn't see much of them after tonight. We both had a few bob left and a few more presents to buy. We had only been in Manchester a few days but it seemed like weeks. Neither of us wanted to go back to Dublin. Bollox. I got this embarrassed feeling all over myself all of a sudden, like you realise your mickey is hanging out and everyone is looking at you. I had forgotten completely about the hickey on my neck. Jaysus. I hope they didn't think Tommy gave it to me. I slumped down into my seat and pulled my shirt up a bit. Ah, who cares? Worse things had happened today, I thought.

"I get up at six thirty lads. I'll try not to wake yi" Peter said. "I'll give yi a lift tomorrow evening to the train."

"That'll be great Peter" I said.

"I think there's a train about every half hour to Liverpool" he said.

Winnie looked so funny. She had a dressing gown on with her hair in curlers and her two little legs on a little foot stool. She had a big box of Maltesers on her lap and she was stuffing them into her gob by the handful. I caught Tommy's eye for a second and he gave me a big grin. It's really terrible when you want to break your bollox laughing and you can't. "Goodnight boys" Peter said and off he went to bed. Winnie had finished the Maltesers. Then a big

Toblerone appeared on the scene. The bleeding savage, I thought to myself. I felt great. I think Tommy did too. There was a late night movie on. It was called "Casablanca" and Humphrey Bogart was in it. "It's my favourite movie" Winnie said as she shovelled a lump of Toblerone into her mouth. Tommy was secretly making fat faces at me.

When you're in good humour you just want to laugh. A bit of chocolate was melting down the side of her mouth. My Ma never looked like this. I suppose her son thinks she's great coz she's his Ma but there's nothing like your own mother. My Ma was forty and much nicer looking than Winnie and she didn't stuff her face with chocolate like that. I think I'll buy her something special, I thought to myself. I was getting tired and could feel my eyes shutting. "I'm going to bed. Goodnight Winnie" I said.

"Goodnight Marty".

"I'm going to watch a bit more of this" Tommy said.

I was really tired. I lay there looking at the pictures on the wall. A bit of shopping tomorrow and then home on the boat tomorrow night.

I had the weirdest dream. It was the end of the world. I was the only person on the earth that knew and nobody would believe me. I was going around telling everybody and when I'd leave their house and look back the house would melt and collapse. Bollox, it was raining when I woke up in the morning. Tommy was still fast asleep. It was ten to eight. Peter would be gone to work. I had a look through a book that was on a little table at the side of my bed. It was a book about the Busby Babes. On the inside of the cover was written "To Mum and Dad Xmas '66". It had photographs in the middle of it, pictures of players that were killed in the plane crash. It was February 1958 that it happened. One of the players, Liam Whelan was from Ireland. It must have been a terrible disaster. Nearly the whole football team wiped out. Other people were killed as well.

Tommy woke up. He farted. I replied with one.

"What are yi reading?" he said.

"It's called "How to eat a stone of Maltesers in one go" I said.

Tommy pulled the blankets over his head and started making pig sounds.

"Shut up for fuck sake" I said. "She'll hear yi".

"I don't hear any noise in the kitchen" Tommy said.

"What?!! No breakfast ready" I said. "What kind of a poxy hotel is this?"

"I'll have mine in bed today" Tommy said.

"To hell, let's make it ourselves" I said.

We dragged on some clothes and went downstairs. Monday morning. We could hear Winnie snoring.

"Let's make her a breakfast and bring it up to her" Tommy said.

"Yeah, and the two of us will get in beside her" I said.

We did a few boiled eggs and toast and sat looking out at the rain. "We better buy them something today" I said.

"OK" Tommy said.

I can imagine, I thought to myself, a small box of Dairy Milk.

Winnie came down in a pink dressing gown.

"I never heard you boys getting up."

I poured her out a cup of tea.

"Oh, bloody rain" she said "and Peter's working outdoors today. You boys will get drenched in the city. I suppose you don't care though" she said. "Make sure you're back before five. Peter will bring you to the train."

We headed off with a big umbrella Winnie lent us. We had about ten pounds each left. We had our tickets for the boat which included the train to Liverpool. There were only a few people on the bus. Two old men were talking about the price of beer and cigarettes.

"Young people have it so lucky these days."

Jaysus, is that all old people ever say, I thought. The bus pulled into a big bus station. I was a bit sad because we would be going home today and of course it would have to be raining. We headed straight for Woolworths. A Monty Python book for Joan. She loves that programme on the BBC. I did too although half the time I didn't understand it. A poster of Jethro Tull for David, not that there was any bleeding room left on the wall. A few more English sweets for Derek and wooden thing with a picture of Manchester United and all little hooks for hanging your keys on for Ma and Da. Tommy bought his Ma and Da a plate to hang on the wall with a picture of Manchester Cathedral on it.

"Let's get Winnie and Peter something now" I said. "What does Peter smoke?" I asked.

"I didn't know he smoked" Tommy said.

"He had one in the car on the way home from the match" I said. "Rothmans they were. Why don't we get Peter some fags and Winnie some flowers?"

"OK, but let's get them on the way home. I'm not walking around Manchester with a bunch of bleedin' flowers all day" Tommy said.

I had to get Catherine something. We went to the underground markets and had a gawk.

"Di yi think Catherine would like a Harrington Tommy?"

"She'd bleedin' love one" he said.

Right. That was it. They were on special at a Paki stall for three quid. A black one with tartan lining. She'll love me now I thought. Tommy bought United scarves and badges and another Manchester United tee-shirt. We walked around looking at everything, wishing we had more money left.

"You're hickey's disappearing" Tommy said.

"It's nothing compared to the worry Des has" I said.

"No point in getting him condoms then" said Tommy, smiling. He had a sick sense of humour sometimes.

"Maybe some nappies instead" I said.

"Ah stop, for fuck sake."

"It won't be funny when we get home" I said.

We were both getting hungry so we went back to Woolworths café. We got on a queue. Like in Dublin they had oul' ones serving. This lady was pouring out a big stew onto someone's plate, it looked like liquid shite.

"They must be feedin' the dogs" Tommy said.

A woman heard him and didn't look too happy. "You're real bloody funny aren't yi?"

Tommy went scarlet. I shuttled on and got sausages, beans and chips. Nice one Tommy.

"Fuck. I didn't think she heard me."

We sat near the window looking at the people getting pissed on. "Jaysus, I've got three pound left" I said.

"I haven't got much more than yi" Tommy said.

"At least we have return tickets for the train. It was good fun though, wasn't it?" I said. "I can't wait to wear me clobber and see the jealous faces. I bet they'll all be goin' to England now."

I was really missing Catherine now. I was thinking about all the things I'd done and she'll probably never know. I hope this bleeding love bite is gone by Saturday. The last day of your holiday is always crap. I wonder if they sell loose cigarettes here I thought because that's all Tommy will be buying for Peter.

"Hello boys, how are yis?"

A Dublin accent. The lady we met on Friday from Finglas who was cleaning the tables.

"Bought the whole of Manchester, have you?"

"We've had great fun" Tommy said "except for the match of course."

"Me husband was delighted, him being a City fan. When are yis heading back?"

"Tonight" I said.

"Back to dirty Dublin, eh? Will they ever clean it up?"

"Manchester is much cleaner" I said.

"I suppose your cases are packed with French Letters?" she said laughing. "Every time I go back for a visit, my sister Sylvia gives me the orders for bucket loads of them. No wonder there was eleven kids in our family. Terrible isn't it. Imagine not bein' able to buy them. Will Ireland ever change?"

Where were ours I thought? Oh yeah, in the inside pocket of our crombies.

"There'd be less unwanted pregnancies in Ireland if they had them."

We both looked at each other.

"We've got a friend in a bit of trouble" I said.

"Ah you're joking son. Yi know every week I meet some poor unfortunate who've just arrived and had either come here to get away from all their family or to have an abortion. It's not right. Anyway, you two boys have a good trip home."

Then she did the most amazing thing. She handed us a pound and said to get some sweets on the boat. It was like an Auntie when you were young and they would give you money for ice cream. "Thanks missus" Tommy said. "Yeah, thank you" I said.

"Jaysus, that was nice of her wasn't it?"

"It's Ok missus, we don't need any sweets but we'll get a tab of acid instead" I said.

Tommy was laughing again.

"I wonder does me Ma and Da use condoms?" I said. "There's only four of us. They hardly only did it four times since they got married."

"Catholics can't use them" Tommy said. "At least they're not supposed to but if loads of Irish girls are havin' abortions that can't be right either."

Tommy was getting all intelligent now. We were having a serious conversation.

"Do you believe in God and all that?" he asked me.

"I dunno, but I always wonder about other people who aren't Catholics. I mean, are they wrong and we're right or maybe we're wrong. I mean, how do you got through your whole life only getting your hole four times? Like are the Jews all wrong?"

"Yeah I know" said Tommy. "Are all English people wrong for taking the pill and does it mean they'll all go to hell?"

"You know when you're robbin' something and yi think someone's watchin' yi, is there really someone watchin' yi or do they tell us all these things just to make us afraid."

"My uncle Frank hasn't gone to Mass for years" Tommy said. "Now, will he go to Hell?"

"Jaysus, Dave Allen is going to Hell" I said. "He really takes the piss out of religion, doesn't he?"

Would I go to Hell for touching Catherine's diddy I wondered. It was getting late.

"We better get the fags and flowers. I'm burstin'" I said.

We went to the jacks. We were having a piss and somebody was in one of the toilets with the door locked. The door opened a tiny bit and closed again. Tommy looked at me.

"Would either of you two boys like to earn 50 pence."

We both grabbed our bags and then Tommy grabbed the rubbish bin and threw it over the cubicle. We ran out the door and all you could hear was him effin' and blindin'. A big negro woman with a mop and bucket was cleaning up under a table.

"There's a queer in the toilet" Tommy said to her as we went past.

She said nothing but just stared at the two of us as we went down the escalator.

"Jaysus, a bleedin' puff" I said.

"Yi know, I could have done with the money" Tommy said laughing.

"Just when I thought all the excitement was over" I said. "The dirty bastard."

It reminded me of stories of the Iveagh Baths that my Ma always warned me about when we were kids. I think we were both really terrified. When something like this happens to you in Dublin, it's not that bad but when you're in a different country you get a real fright. A lady was selling flowers from a stall and we bought a huge bunch for 75 pence. We went into a shop and Tommy asked for 20 Rothmans.

"For Jaysus sake Tommy, 20? Get him 50" I said.

He didn't look too happy but he got them anyway. The lady wrapped them in brown paper for us and sellotaped a little thank you card. We were back on the bus and heading back to Chorlton-cum-Hardy. I ended up holding the flowers. A gang of girls got on and giggled at me all the way to where we got off.

"Are you hungry?" I asked as we walked up the road.

"Not really" said Tommy.

"Well I bet Winnie has a huge bleedin' dinner ready."

"Ah shit, probably" said Tommy. "You can give her the flowers."

"No, you do it."

"No, you."

"Ok" I said. "I'll do it."

Winnie answered the door and was delighted with the flowers. "You shouldn't have boys. It was a pleasure havin' you both." I felt really guilty for laughing at her. She was really nice. Peter came down the stairs. He was home early and I gave him the fags.

"That's very nice boys. You'll have to come and say hello to us in October at the wedding" he said.

Unbelievably Winnie had nothing made in the kitchen.

"Would you like some fish and chips for tea?"

"No thanks Winnie" I said. "We're both stuffed. A cup of tea will do fine."

"Ok boys."

We went upstairs and packed. We were both feeling a bit sad. The dirty magazine dropped out of Tommy's case.

"Bollox, where'll I hide this?"

He opened his case and found a little bit of torn material on the bottom and stuffed it inside the lining.

"I'll rent it out to everyone at the building site" he said. We brought everything down to the hall and had our tea watching the tele. Blue Peter was on. Winnie had made us sandwiches and had wrapped them in silver foil.

"They're for the boat boys. So yi won't get hungry."

I was really sorry for slagging her now. We said our goodbyes and thank you to Winnie and headed off with Peter in the car. He gave us a hand into the railway station with our cases and then stuffed a pound into both our pockets. Jaysus, more money. "Be careful boys."

We got in the carriage and waved goodbye. The train was packed with people. In my head I was already planning my next trip back to Manchester. We both fell asleep and woke up in Liverpool's Lime Street Station. It was getting dark and there was a gang outside the café we went into on the way here. A coach said B&I Boat and we got on board as quick as we could. So our little hollier to England was almost over. It was only a few days but it seemed like weeks. We weren't talking as much as when we were coming over. We both just wanted to close our eyes and be in Dublin again.

There weren't many people on the boat going back. We had loads of room in the TV room. I just wanted to put on all me clobber and walk around Dublin with people gawking at me. So did Tommy. The boat pulled out and we were off. One of my Ma's neighbours daughters, Peggy Lynch, saw us and came over to talk to us. She was in England with a swimming team. We told her all about Old Trafford and all the nice bits we did. It's nice to see someone you know although at home I probably wouldn't ever say hello to her. We got tea and ate our sandwiches and soon the pair of us fell fast asleep. It was half six and the boat was coming into Dublin when we woke up. I could see the two Ringsend chimneys. We grabbed our cases and stood in the queue half asleep.

"Me Da is always on time for everything" Tommy said.

I farted, a sneaky one and it was rotten. Nobody said anything but you knew by their faces they got it. I was looking forward to seeing everyone again. Catherine, Ma, Da, Joan, Derek, David, Tony, Mick and poor ould Des. Des.............

November 1972

It was lashing rain, belting off the front window of the upstairs of the bus from Ballymun to the city. It was packed. Friday evening, nearly everyone smoking and coughing at the same time. The last Friday of November. Shitty, miserable weather. I thought of summer and us all lying out in Mooney's field, drinking flagons and those real late evenings. They seemed like years ago. It was well and truly winter now. The oul' fellah sitting beside me has the Herald and the back page headline reads "United at home to Saints". I pretended not to be reading his paper. There's a knack to it. There was a picture of Georgie Best as well. Who were the Saints, I thought. Every English team had a nickname. I learned that since August. United were the Red Devils, Arsenal were the Gunners, Leeds United were the Wankers and Liverpool were even worse. It seems if you follow United you have to hate every other team. Someone upstairs on the bus had a terrible cough, like real phlegmy.

I lit up a Major. I was bleeding starving. I was working on a building site in Ballymun and covered in muck. I had twelve pound or so in my pay packet. The whole weekend was ahead. The oul' fellah was reading every bit of the sport page, holding it about six inches from his mush. I never read the sport pages. Maybe someday I'll be reading about Mick on the back page. The man who was writing things down during the summer at Mick's games was a football scout for Liverpool Football Club and Mick got a letter to say they were offering him a trial after Christmas. He would be going over with his Da and had to stay about two weeks so they could have a gawk at him. The lucky bollox. Imagine if he makes it. He'll have a sports car and have girls hanging off each arm and we'll see him on tele. He told us he'd miss us all though. Good on him. He must be a great player I thought. He said we could all go over and stay with him and go to the games if he makes the big time. I'd know someone famous at last.

"Fares please".

The traffic was shite. What would I do tonight? Maybe the Loft, maybe the flix. Everyone was talking about a movie called "The Last Picture Show". It was in black and white but this girl strips off and jumps into a swimming pool and you can see her fanny! Two skinheads got on the bus and came upstairs. They were heading off for the night by the look of them. I had much better clothes than them. I had been back to Manchester at the end of September to see United beat Derby County 3 – 0. I bought even more gear then. I had a complete suedeheads wardrobe now. My hair was growing a bit longer. He was reading the funnies now. Mutt and Jeff. I remember when I was a kid and we used to swap comics. Read it, read it, didn't. Read it, read it, didn't. You brought all your comics to a friend's house and swapped one for one.

This fellah at the end of our road was a bit older than the rest of us and used to buy American comics like Batman and Superman. They were shite and had all these ads on the back pages with words like Zip Code, State and $ signs. We would pretend we wanted one but we really just wanted to see the Bash Street Kids or Dennis the Menace. I loved the Victor or the Hotspur. "Die, you Nippon swine!" "Bonzai" and of course "Achtung". It was always the British bashing the Germans or the Japs. Then you would send away to the Bridgenorth Stamp Company for your stamp "approvals". I never got any back, they were probably worth fuck all anyway.

It was still lashing outside. I was really starving. No work until Monday. Des came into my mind. What a shitty few months he'd had. We had a big meeting in Mooney's when me and Tommy came back from Manchester in August. We all decided that he'd have to tell his Ma and Da and Elaine's as well. It was really hard for him. Her Ma and Da decided to go to Australia and they would rear the child. If Des wanted to follow them out when he was older he could and he'd always be the father.

They were gone over two months. He'd had two letters already from Elaine. She was real homesick and hated Melbourne. He got the feeling that her Dad didn't like her writing to him. We were all pissed a few weeks ago and he got real emotional and started crying. He said that he hated the idea of Elaine having a baby and he wouldn't be there. It was his child as well. He had changed so much. I told my Ma and Da all about it and Ma said she felt they should have stayed in Ireland and that it wouldn't be worth all the problems going to Australia.

I got off and walked down O'Connell Street to get the 50 bus in Fleet Street. It wasn't raining hard now, just miserable drizzle. Friday evening, dark, people going home from work, people heading out early, buses everywhere. It was exactly half past five by the clock over Clery's. Dublin had had so many bomb scares lately. Imagine if one went off now, I thought to myself. Henry Street had its Christmas lights up. It was only four weeks away. I was going to buy Catherine a watch.

"Herald or Press", the same fellah outside Easons selling paper and magazines. One of the plumbers I worked with does the English pools with him. He sends them up to Belfast every week because you can't do them in the Republic of Ireland. Jaysus, the Liffey stank. I passed over O'Connell Bridge and saw this gang coming towards me with United scarves and I recognised one of them. His name was Peter and he was on the boat with us in September. He stopped and started talking to me. They were heading over to see United play Southampton. Aha, they must be the Saints, I thought. They were going to a pub down the quays and meeting another gang.

"We went over last month to see them play Spurs. It was terrible. Martin Peters scored four fucking goals and United only scored one."

"C'mon Peter, we're getting soaked. See yi again."

"Good luck."

Lucky bastards, I thought. Fleet Street was packed as usual. A queue me bollox. It was every man for himself. "Marty." I heard a voice. It was Tommy. He was way ahead of me on the queue. I sneaked up slowly. I could see the sack of sticks beside him. Two 50 buses came in together. A mad bleeding rush. The two of us pushed our way on to the first bus. Why couldn't they just have enough buses. This had been going on for years. I used to love when the buses would go on strike and we were kids and the Army trucks would come out. We would get on them and pretend we were soldiers heading off to war. It was much more exciting than being on a bus. You could hear the same conversation every trip. "Why do we need CIE anyway when we have the Army. Maybe it's a pay rise they want. My husband's been in his job years and he never gets a rise. I'll give them a bleedin' rise. With me boot."

"And so this is Christmas... and what have you done... Another year older.... And a new one just begun" Eddie Kelly was down the back of the bus singing. He was slightly retarded and everywhere he went he always sang. It was John Lennon's latest song for Christmas. Eddie worked in a factory somewhere and lived around the corner from me. "C'mon everybody, sing." You could see all the embarrassed faces on the bus. "What are yi doing tonight, Marty?"

"I dunno, maybe I'll just go up to Catherine's. I'm too bleeding tired" I said. "What are you doing?"

"Goin' to Bingo with me Ma."

I said nothing. When I think of all the things we got up to in the last year and he's going to Bingo with his Ma. Only Tommy could do that. Sit there in his Wranglers and his Doc's and braces shoutin' "Check" and "Legs Eleven".

"Why don't yi come with Catherine?" he said.

Is he serious I thought.

"Ah, I'll give it a miss" I said.

Past Dolphins' Barn. One or two of the shops had Christmas lights up already. My Da hated that. He only liked Christmas Eve and Christmas Day.

"Christmas, don't make me sick. It's all bleedin' money. The tele brain-washes yi."

"Ah, don't spoil it" Ma would say.

Derek was getting Action Man. The rest of us just got money now. It was better. You could buy what you liked then. Gilbert had a new LP out and I was going to buy it at Christmas. It was called Back to Front and he had a song in the charts called Clair from the album. Catherine loved it. It was nearly Christmas and the year just about over. So much had happened to us all since last Christmas. Especially Des. Past Crumlin hospital. How many times had I passed it over the years I thought.

"A very Merry Christmas......" Eddie was still singing.

"Aw, shut the fuck up" a voice from downstairs shouted. Eddie just got louder. Tommy was cracking up. It started pissing down again. The two of us got off the bus in the village. Tommy looked so funny with his bag of sticks over his shoulder, like Father Christmas. We stood in the bus shelter for a few minutes talking. Tommy had broken it off with his girlfriend, Betty, a few weeks ago and it didn't seem to bother him much.

"I often think of Mags and Liz" he said. "That was a great hollier. It seems so long ago doesn't it? Did yi ever tell Catherine about any of it?"

"Naw, just the nice bits and the bits I made up. It would have been all off it I'd told her about Mags. It'll be shite next year though."

"Why?" Tommy asked.

"Well none of us know where Des will be and Mick will probably be in Liverpool and Tony doesn't know what he'll be doin'."

Tony's boss was thinking of selling up his butchers business and going to live in Canada and he wanted Tony to go with them for a year or so to see what he thought about it.

"Yeah, Jaysus the gang is all breakin' up I suppose" Tommy said.

"Fuck it" I said "let's all meet tomorrow night and get pissed somewhere."

"Yeah" Tommy's eyes lit up.

"I'll make the phone calls OK."

"OK" Tommy said.

"We'll head off early and see if we can get into some boozer. If not we'll get some flagons."

We hadn't done that for months. We were both getting real excited now.

"Are yi workin' in the morning?"

"No" I said.

"OK. I'll call up to yi" Tommy said.

"Have yi still got that nudie book?" I asked.

"Naw, some bollox robbed it out of me bag on the building site. Yi know what labourers are like if they know there's a porno book around. Holy Catholic Ireland me arse.They were all like flies around shite when they knew I had a magazine with tits and fannys in it.Anyway, I'll see yi in the morning."

"See yi Tommy."

Off he went like the Hunchback of Notre Dame. He didn't even have to talk, just the things he did would make you laugh. I was soaked to the bleeding skin walking home. Most of the shops in the village had their Christmas decorations up. Why don't they have Christmas in the summer I thought. Christmas is always real happy but the weather is always crap. Something kept going through my head. I was working that day with Peter Byrne, a plumber who was about fifty. We were talking about something and he said to me "For fuck sake son, make sure you're still not doing this when you're my age or yi'll end up bitter and twisted." What did he mean? Ah well, I'm only 16. I'm not going to worry about things like that. Into the house. The smell of fish and chips in the air. Dad always said the same thing every Friday.

"Well son, did the golden eagle shite today?"

"Yes Dad. Of course I got paid."

I gave Mam her £4 and my £2 to save and the rest was mine. I gave Catherine a quick ring. She didn't want to go out, the weather was lousy. I was to call up to her. Yes, your Majesty I thought.

"Can I have me pay?" Derek asked.

I gave him 20p every week but to get it he had to do something in the house.

"What did you do for Mam then?"

"I took Jackie for a walk."

Jackie was our Cocker Spaniel.

"Where did yi bring him?" I asked.

"Jaysus, what you have to do for 20p" David piped in.

"Well you give him 20p then."

David had just started a carpentry apprenticeship.

"Now you two give it up" Ma said. "Your dinner's ready."

Long ray and chips, my favourite. Nobody made fish and chips like me Ma.

"Your Dad has something to yell you all" Ma said.

Silence.Shit, everything went through my mind. He's got cancer, they're splitting up – no they get on good. Mam looked around and made sure Derek hadn't come into the room for his dinner yet.

"We won £1000 in the Prize Bonds" Dad said with a big smile on his face.

There was that little silence while we let it sink in. Immediately I thought how much are we all getting. Joan jumped up and gave Dad a big hug. Me or David didn't know what to say. "For God's sake don't tell Derek. He's too young to know and besides at that age he'll tell the whole street." Ma said.

"What are yis gonna do with it? I said.

"Well, we've been think about it. We're gonna change the car, have a holiday in Spain and give the three of you £50 each."

"Brilliant" I said.

We were all so excited. Fifty bleeding pound I thought. I'll save it. Bollox, I'll go to England and see Bowie. No I'll spend it all on clothes. No I'll buy a motor bike.No I'll.... Derek came in. I threw him 50 pence.

"There's a bonus this week Derek."

Ma smiled.

"Fifty pence. Look Ma."

His eyes were lit up like Marty Feldman's. We all wanted to talk about it but we have to shut up with Derek around. The doorbell rang. Derek ran out. It was his pal Paul from across the road. He had his bag of Lego under his arm and the two of them went into the front room.

"Come back and eat your dinner Derek."

"Can I bring it in here with me?"

"Ah let him love" Da said, winking.

He grabbed his plate and went back in.

"Are yi gonna give Derek anything Ma?" I asked.

"We'll probably buy him a transistor. He has his eye on one in the village. It's yellow and real modern looking."

Derek had started listening to Pop music a lot and knew all the gossip on everyone. He has posters of the Sweet all around his bed along with the Osmonds. Ma and Da had never been to Spain but lots of their friends had.

"How di yi find out?" I asked.

"I checked the numbers on Wednesday evening like I always do and nearly died of fright when our numbers matched. I must have checked it ten times and then I got your Da to check them. Then yesterday morning Da rang the Prize Bond office and it was definite. They will send us out a cheque next week."

"Imagine if it was £50000" I said.

"I'd buy a house on Howth Hill" Mam said.

"I suppose you've no champagne" Joan asked. "We should be celebrating."

Ma took out the sherry from under the sink and her and Dad and Joan had a little glass.

"Is this the stuff you drink in Mooney's on Saturday night?" Joan said, trying to be funny.

Dad smiled.

"Now give it up" Ma said.

Me and David were given a shandy with loads of lemonade. Derek came back in.

"Ma can we have some lemonade? Why are youse all drinkin'?"

He had those big inquisitive eyes on him.

"Dad won a million pounds on the Prize Bonds" I said.

He stared at Ma not saying anything with that 'Are they jokin' or not?' look on his face.

Mam gave him two glasses of Taylor Keith lemonade "and don't spill it on the carpet." He was too interested in the lemonade to think any more about the money.

"For God's sake don't go telling anyone you lot. Yi know how jealous people can get" Ma said.

Shit I couldn't wait to tell all the guys I thought. Maybe I better not though. They'd all fucking hound me for some money.

"Now we'll have to trust yis all if we got to Spain" Mam said.

A free house I thought. Loads of garglin'. Great. Dad started singing "oh, this year I'm off to sunny Spain hey viva the Spaniards."

"That's not the words yi eejit" Ma said.

Derek and his pal Paul were singing in the front room "I'll be your long haired lover from Liverpool and I'll do anything you ask."

"I had to buy the record for him yesterday" Ma said.

The Osmonds youngest brother, little Jimmy, had a new song. It was absolute shite. Only seven year olds could like that crap. They were singing it together. Ma said they used the two candles off the fireplace as microphones. I went up to my bedroom thinking about the £50 I'd be getting. I had a few new pictures on my side on the wall, a big poster of United, a new one of Bowie, a big one of Gary Glitter. I picked up the New Musical Express. It was a great magazine with loads of gossip. There was an article about Bowie in it. I lay on the bed and had a read. He was currently in America working with a fellah called Iggy Pop. There was a picture of him in a studio somewhere with this Iggy Pop. Someday I'd get to see him I thought. £50. I was bleeding rich. I couldn't wait for tomorrow night. We'd get pissed. Ma and Da were going to a Christmas do so they wouldn't be home until late. Mam came upstairs and knocked on the door.

"Marty, don't say anything to Catherine, OK? People can be funny."

She meant Catherine's Ma and Da. They were culchies and Mam and Dad were always cagey about telling country people anything, especially Dad. He just didn't trust them. If they didn't have a Dublin accent they were different.

"Ok Ma."

"Isn't it great" Ma said.

"Yeah Ma."

She was over the moon. I could see by the look on her face. She had been talking about Spain all year and how she'd love to go someday. Ma and Da loved the sun and had spent a week in the summer in a caravan in Wexford with Derek. They always came home real brown. We used to all go to the beach for holidays when we were kids. Dad would leave us down in a van at the weekend and then he would go back to Dublin and work all week. Ma would be stuck with us all week in a caravan. If it rained we would stay in the caravan and stare out the window or play snap. Then we'd kill each other when we got bored. No tele or radio. No toilet. We had to go across the field to a horrible wooden outside toilet that had a strong smell of creosote. When you had a shite the smell of creosote and shite would make you sick. Then there would never be enough paper. We would have to go to a pump for water for the tea or washing your hands and face. They must have been great holidays though because we always cried our eyes out all the way home.

"Phone, Marty." Joan called.

It was Mick. He had met Tommy and heard about Saturday night. He was all on for it. We would meet outside O'Hagan's at seven. He'd tell Des and I'd tell Tony. I went back upstairs and changed. I looked out the bathroom window. The rain had stopped but it was really cold. I had to go up to Catherine. I was going out with her for almost a year. I'd love to tell her about the £50 but I better not. Not yet anyway. I'll call around to Tony first and tell him about tomorrow night. Tony had started going out with a girl from Crumlin a few months ago and was mad about her. She had left school this year and was working in Dunnes Stores in the city. I hope he hasn't any plans made for Saturday night.

"See yiz later. I'm going up to Catherine's."

"Remember Marty, keep your gob shut" said Ma.

Derek and Paul were still singing in the front room. "I didn't know I loved you till I saw you Rock and Roll" Gary Glitter. It's amazing the things you do when you're young. Imagine me and Tony or Tommy singing into candles in the front room. How quick you change when you get older. If Mick made the big time with his football in Liverpool he'd have to walk out in front of thousands of people every week. Jaysus. I walked around to Tony's house. It was freezing. The rain had gone. I had me crombie coat on with the velvet collar, jeans turned up at the ends and me Doc's. Tony was at his front gate talking to someone. It was Tommy Gleeson.

"How're yi Marty, long time no see."

Yeah, I thought to myself, because you've been in juvenile prison. Gleeson was caught with a bag of marijuana in the village and got two months in Mountjoy. He was telling Tony all about it as if it was a huge big adventure. The fucking eejit. When he was going he said to us if we ever want some to give him a shout.

"That gobshite will never learn" Tony said.

I told him about Saturday night and he was all excited. He wasn't seeing his girlfriend, Carol, until Sunday night so was on for it. He'd grown his hair a bit, we all had. Skinheads were dying out a bit. It was all suedeheads and boot boys now.

"Did yi see Top of the Pops last night?" Tony said.

"Yeah. 'My Ding-a-ling'. What the fuck was that? Slade's one is great though. Goodbye T Jane. It'll be a number one for Christmas."

"Are we gonna to try a pub tomorrow night?" Tony asked.

"Yeah, it's a bit cold to be drinkin' in Mooney's field. I hope Des doesn't get all sad again" I said. "His baby's due in January, he was telling me."

Tony started humming Skippy.

"You're a sick bastard Tony."

The two of us started laughing.

"What about Canada Tony?"

The butchers shop was up for sale.

"He hopes to be goin' early next year. I haven't made me mind up yet though. I'm only 16. It's a fuckin' huge thing to do. And I'd be livin' with them as well. He has a son about two years older than us. I can't stand him. He's a smart arse."

Catherine's younger sister walked by us, big smile on her face. It was Friday. Her Da would have given her pocket-money and she was off to O'Hagan's. "Are yi comin' up after Marty?"

"Yeah, keep me some sweets, Ok. I better go Tony."

"Ok. See yi tomorrow."

I walked through the village. Eight o'clock, Friday evening. The usual scumbags outside the chipper.

"Got any odds?"

Joe Nevin was there. I hated him. He was one evil prick. I quickly walked past. I knew if he saw me there would be loads of hassle. I crossed the road and looked back. He was standing waiting for a bus on his own. I stopped and got an idea.

Something came over me all of a sudden. I stood in behind the big hedge that was outside the vegetable shop and picked up a nice little stone. I was a super shot with a stone when I was a kid. He was about fifty yards away. I took aim and threw it and immediately walked quickly away in the other direction. I kept walking for about half a minute.Everything goes through your head.I could feel me heart racin'. Then I looked back. He was down on his hunkers with a few people around him. I was grinning from ear to ear. All those years of hassle from that poxbottle, going to school then to the dances in the village. I could never fight him. He would pull out a knife or a broken bottle. £50 and now getting Nevin as well. It was a great Friday so far. I had to know though. Mrs McKenna, a friend of my Ma's was coming toward me. I started tying my shoelace and then as she came past I said hello.

"How are yi Marty? Still doing a line with Mrs Dwyers daughter?"

"Yeah Mrs McKenna."

I started walking back with her. My heart was thumping. I acted real innocent when we passed the chipper. Nevin was sitting on a chair in the shop with blood streaming down his face from the side of his head. A few people were standing with him. Mrs McKenna looked in. My God, there must've been a fight. I was a bit surprised at my own badness. I didn't care though. Take that you fucking bollox. Now how do you like it? I felt great. Someday I'll tell me kids this story. Jaysus, what if he dies? Naw, he won't. Probably a few stitches.

"How's your Mam and Dad."

"Great Mrs McKenna."

They've just won £1000, I thought.

"Are yi workin' away."

"Yeah, I'm on me second year now."

"Great. Your Mam was telling me about your pal from Crumlin going over to Liverpool. That's marvellous, isn't it?"

"It is Mrs McKenna. He's really lookin' forward to it."

"Anyway, goodbye Marty. God Bless."

She had the little pull along shopping trolley all the women had. A real Dub. There was something real nice about talking to them. They always asked you about yourself and your Ma and Da. I knocked at Catherine's door. She answered it.

"Will yi come for a walk first?" she said. "I've got to go to Auntie Maureen's house with a Christmas cake recipe for her."

She had her dog on a lead, a little corgi called Sammy.

"Ok."

Her Aunty lived about a mile away in Kimmage. She had her blue school gaberdeen on and a Manchester United scarf. I had brought it back from Old Trafford. It had "There's only one United" written on it. I held her hand. It was freezing. She was nearly fifteen. She told me all about school and her friends. She didn't hang around with Cathy anymore.After all my worryin' about Butlins nothing happened.She should have been more worried than me! Anyway, Cathy's gone. No loss. She was really coming between us. Catherine put her hand in my Crombie pocket. It was warm now. I started singing. "John, I'm only dancing, she turns me on, I'm only dancing, don't get me wrong."

"Is he really a queer?" Catherine asked.

"I don't know. I'll ring him and ask him. Mark Bolan is supposed to be as well. I think they pretend just to get all the publicity."

Sammy was doing a shite outside a gate.

"They'll step into that if they come out in the dark" I said.

I started laughing to myself. When Tommy and I were kids, we used to follow the breadman around when he used to come with his horse and cart. We used to pick up the horse-shite with a shovel when it was still fresh and put it in a paper bag, then we'd put on a doorstep; light the paper bag and ring the bell and run away. When someone answered the door they'd automatically stamp on it to put it out and get a foot full of shite.

"We're all meeting tomorrow night" I said. "We haven't for a while."

"Where are yis going?" Catherine asked.

"I dunno. I think we all just want to see how Des is. He's been really upset lately. She's due her baby in January. Des got a letter from her last week. She took a photo of herself showing off her fat belly."

"Did she?" Catherine said.

"Yeah, and she said they've been in the swimming pool a few times because the weather was getting real hot. It's weird, isn't it. She's in Australia and Des is here."

"Wait and see when the baby's born." Catherine said. "He'll be really unhappy then."

"When she gets some money together she's going to try to ring him from a phone box."

I really wanted to tell her about the £50 but I didn't. I wanted to tell her about Nevin but I didn't. It started to spit rain again. We got to her Aunt's house. She brought us both in and gave us tea. She's Catherine's Da's sister. Her husband Paddy was a train driver. He was working late. She was delighted with the cake recipe. She was really funny. She would say anything to you. Catherine told me she was a bit of a rebel growing up in Wicklow.

"Jesus, Marty you're like Al Capone with the velvet collar. Is that all the fashion nowadays?"

"Yes, Maureen." I said.

She had one daughter called Veronica. She was a bit of a rebel too. She was twenty and drank like a fish. She was going to University and wanted to be a teacher.

"Marty, have a look at this."

She brought me upstairs to Veronica's room. The whole room was covered in posters, but no ordinary ones. Ban the Bomb, Make Love not War, No EEC. She had a big one with a fellah with a black balaclava over his face and a tee shirt with England get out of Ireland written on it. I said nothing.

"Have yi ever seen anything like it? Most girls her age have Donny Osborne or your man Cassidy on their walls. She used to have all them but since she started going to Trinity all these are appearing."

Catherine gave me a funny look. There was a poster with a man lying on the ground with blood coming out his head and a priest blessing him. " Remember Bloody Sunday" was written at the bottom of it. I'll never forget that day. We were coming out of the Loft and there was a load of busmen yapping at a bus stop and Mick heard one of them saying there had been a massacre up the north. We were on the bus home and the news was spreading like wildfire. A woman got on at Dolphin's Barn and told everyone upstairs that loads of people had been shot in Derry. It was all on the news when I got home. At least twelve people had been shot dead by the paratroopers. The next day nobody went to work and thousands of people went into town and burned down the British Embassy. I remember me Da looking at the report on TV and saying that this was the start of something terrible. There had been loads of people killed since then.

"It's probably a phase she's going through" Maureen said.

There was a black beret beside her bed. I still said nothing but I had a funny feeling Veronica was getting involved with Sinn Fein or something like that. We finished our tea. Maureen gave Catherine a pound.

"Get yourselves some chips on the way home."

Lovely I thought. We went home by the village. It was still drizzling. Four scrubbers came towards us with their arms all linked together. They were singing "Loop-di-love". They pushed straight through us.

"Fuckin' poshies" one of them said.

"Wagons" Catherine replied.

"What did you say?" a big ugly bitch with short blond hair said. We kept walking. Catherine looked frightened. That was it. I'd had enough. I took care of Nevin earlier so I didn't care anymore. I turned around and the four of them were standing still, ready for a row. I took the lead off the dog and walked straight at them. My heart was thumping.

"Marty, don't" Catherine said.

They ran, screaming. I was so fucking relieved. Catherine didn't know whether to laugh or cry. When I thought about it I was really going to hit the big one. We hurried on to the chipper. I wondered where they were from. They didn't really get a good look at us so I wasn't too worried. Catherine still looked frightened. We got chips and spiceburgers and two Fantas. We sat outside O'Hagans for a few minutes. An exciting night so far I thought. You could hear shouting and singing coming out of the pubs. Friday night, everybody paid. The spiceburger was too cold so I gave it to Sammy. Someday I'll come back and kill all the bastards in the village. You should be able to walk around without being hassled all the time. I wondered how Nevin was. I gave Catherine a hug and a kiss. I could see she got a fright.

"Let's go" I said.

Tony was standing at his front door talking to his next-door neighbour. We went over to him. His neighbour, Tommy Clarke, was a bit pissed and stared at Catherine.

"Are you Denis Dwyer's daughter, coz you're the spittin' image of him."

"Yeah I am, how di yi know him?" Catherine asked.

"I work with him in Lomans."

Catherine's Da was in charge of the maintenance in Lomans Mental Hospital.

"He told me his daughter is doing a line with Tony Curran's son." He belched. "Scuse me. Where did an ugly bollox like your Da get a little beauty like you?"

Catherine started laughing nervously.

"Good night now." He staggered off down the path, then he let a monstrous fart. "'Scuse me."

The three of us sat on Tony's step and coiled up laughing.

"The dirty swine." Catherine said.

"He's a mad bastard." Tony said. "He's had about twelve pints yi know. Where were yis?"

"Catherine's Aunty Maureen's house in Kimmage." I told him about the 4 bitches.

"I'd have done the same" Tony said. "I was in the chipper tonight and Gino was tellin' me about Joe Nevin."

Gino was a real fat Italian who owned the Chipper.

"What about him?" I asked.

This should be good I thought.

"Well, seemingly" (Tony loved using big words like seemingly and his favourite one was fortunately) "he came staggerin' in the door with blood all over his face and clothes. They sat him down on a chair. What happened was a bus went past and must have driven over a stone and it flew up and hit him on the side of the head."

There was a little pause then I said "Great, what. Even the fuckin' buses don't like him".

The three of us were delighted.

"It wasn't the bus Tony, I threw it at him".

"Yeah, you'd love to wouldn't yi?" he said.

If only they knew. No. It'll be my secret. It was getting late and drizzling again.

"OK. See yi Catherine."

"See yi Tony."

I left Catherine to the gate. It was too late to go in. The rain was coming down heavy now. I gave her a quick kiss and scarpered home. Dad was fast asleep in front of the tele. An old cowboy movie was on. No one else was in except Ma. I could hear her upstairs.

"Is that you Marty?"

"Yeah Ma."

"Wake your Da up will yi otherwise he'll still be there in the morning."

"OK Ma."

"Oh the dirty gobshite, he didn't put my blanket on!"

"Wake up Da."

"Right, right."

Da woke up all frightened looking.

"You're in trouble Da. Yi didn't put on Ma's blanket."

"Ah shit."

Ma had been out and had even left him a note on the table "Put the blanket on". I could hear him grovelling as he went up the stairs.

"Sorry love, sorry."

I was smiling to myself. Ma came back down, giving out like shite, with a hot water bottle under her arm.

"Yi can ask him to do nothin'. Where did yi go tonight?"

"We had to bring a recipe to Catherine's Aunty Maureen's in Kimmage."

"Isn't it great about the money."

"Yeah, Ma. I don't know what I'll do with my £50."

"I can't wait for Spain. I won't sleep tonight thinking about it."

Jackie was lying on his back on the settee with his four legs up in the air, sort of snoring.

"Jesus, yi can see where he gets that from" Ma said. "Have you work tomorrow?"

"No Ma. I might go into town in the morning."

"OK. Don't stay up too late. David and Derek are asleep. Joan's at a party."

I switched around the channels on the tele. BBC had a late night movie on. *On the Waterfront* with Marlon Brando. I could feel myself getting tired. I was really looking forward to tomorrow night. I brought Jackie up to Da's workshop and gave him his biscuits. The rain had stopped and the sky was completely clear. I saw a falling star and made a wish to myself. I wished someday I'd be married to Catherine and have loads of money and a few kids like me Ma and Da. I switched channels again and there was an American show on BBC2 with Stevie Wonder singing Superstition with a big group of other guys. I sat listening to it and watching him moving his head from side to side as he does.

I liked the song. I loved this. I could tell my friends about a new song I'd heard but they hadn't. I went up to bed. David and Derek were fast asleep.

I slipped into bed and turned on the tranny under the covers. Radio Luxembourg, 208. The sound was good tonight. Some nights were good, some were bad. I could hear Eric Clapton singing *Layla*. The moon was shining in the window. I could see Derek's little posters over his bed. The Sweet, Donny Osmond, Gary Glitter and he had a big poster of the Partridge Family. Elvis was on the radio now singing *"Burning Love"*. I woke up in the middle of the night with me tranny stuck into the back of my neck. I turned it off and went to the jacks and had a piss. Dad was snoring his head off. I got back into bed and fell fast asleep again.

Saturday morning. I love Saturday morning especially if there's no work. David and Derek's beds were empty. I could smell fry. Bowie was looking down at me. It was half past eight. I pulled on me dressing gown and went downstairs. Derek as usual was sprawled across the floor watching cartoons. David was in the kitchen making fried bread dipped in egg. I could see Dad in the workshop. Ma was hanging clothes on the line. It was like a scene from the Waltons. I'll be John Boy I thought. "Leave the pan on David". Meep! Meep! Derek was watching the Road Runner. It was one of those November days. Real cold but a clear blue sky. The last Saturday of the month.

"Morning."

"Hi Mam."

"Make a pot of tea Marty will yi?"

"Ok."

Ma had a bucket of coal in her hand for the fire. What would I do today. Town, yes. Da came in and we all had our breakfast. Derek's hand went right into the box of cornflakes looking for the free toy. He couldn't find it so he got one of Ma's big pots and poured them all out until he found it. He was on his hands and knees on the floor. Ma and Da were in fits of laughing but didn't let him see.

"Look at it, it's stupid" he said.

It was a tiny little dog in a plastic bag. The doorbell rang. Derek ran out and answered it. It was Tommy.

"Come in Tommy" I said.

Mam jumped up and put her teeth in.

"How are yis?"

"Sit down Tommy."

I made him a cup of tea.

"Jaysus, you're up early." I said.

He was dolled up to the nines. Shining Doc's, two tone trousers, Harrington jacket and Ben Sherman shirt.

"Will we got into town?" he said.

"Yeah."

I didn't have to be asked twice. We loved going into town, showing off our clothes and throwing shapes.

"Is your Ma and Da goin' to the dance tonight?" Ma asked Tommy.

The annual community Christmas dance was on tonight.

"Yeah, of course Mrs Curran. They haven't missed it for years." The dance wasn't held locally so they had to get special buses to take them. They always came home about three or four in the morning. It meant I had a free house.

"I'll just be five minutes Tommy."

A quick wash and I was ready for the day. Turned up jeans, black brogues, check shirt and black blazer, now with a new Manchester United crest sewn on.

"Yi'll freeze in that Marty, for Jaysus sake." Da said.

"No I won't. I'm young."

Tommy started laughing.

"Yeah, well yi'll probably get young pneumonia then, not old pneumonia" Da said.

"Yi sound exactly like my old man" Tommy said.

Dad was laughing now.

"Ah, shag off the pair of yis."

"See yis later."

"Good luck" Dad said.

"Tony's working this morning" Tommy said.

"We won't bother calling in then. Have you to get anything?" I said.

"Me Ma wants me to get a cook book in Easons for her sister Eileen. It's her birthday tomorrow."

"When my birthday comes I want a cookery book as well." I said.

"Yeah, so do I" Tommy said "and a book on advanced knitting."

"Do yi remember when you were young and your Ma would bring yi shopping with her and she'd be looking at wallpaper or fuckin' curtains and you'd be standin' there in the shop bored silly" I said.

"Yi feel like crying you're so bored. Or you'd run bleedin' riot thru the shop, jumpin' on all the furniture, pressin' every button you could see." Tommy said.

"The only thing you wanted to know was when you were getting an ice-cream or a packet of Tayto" I said.

The 50 bus came. It was packed with Saturday morning people going into town, probably for the start of their Christmas shopping. We always got stared at because of the clothes we wore. The upstairs of the bus was full of smoke. We both lit up a Major. Tonight should be good I thought. We're all meeting and we hadn't all been together for a while. I told Tommy about Stevie Wonder on the tele last night. He'd heard the song on the radio.

"Have yi heard Slade's new one, Goodbye T Jane?"

"Yeah. It's great" I said. "It'll be No 1 for Christmas. A fellah in work told me they're coming to Dublin early next year. I'll be first on the queue if they do."

The bus was stopped completely now in traffic. Nothing was moving and we were only in Cork Street near the sausage factory.

"Somethin's up" Tommy said.

The bus driver came upstairs and told us there was a bomb scare in Dame Street and the traffic was banked back. We decided to walk. Another fucking bomb scare. It was every weekend now. We walked up to the Liberties and then to Thomas street. All the dealers were out with their stalls full of

Christmas things. Starlights, Cheeky Charlies and decorations. The police were everywhere with loads of army trucks full of soldiers.

We walked past Christchurch Cathedral going towards Dame Street but the police wouldn't let anybody any further. The bomb was at the side of the Olympia. We went back under Christchurch and down the Liffey. I'd forgotten about my £50. I'd love to tell Tommy but I just couldn't. Ma was so excited yesterday. I loved going into town. I think everyone does. Over the Ha'penny Bridge and down the Liffey to O'Connell Street. Jaysus, the two of us looked real smart. We checked ourselves out in every shop window. O'Connell Street was full of people. It was cold but not a cloud in the sky.

Army trucks and police cars were flying around. Although the whole bomb scare thing was terrible there was also something exciting about it. We live in a country where bombs go off with people shooting each other as well. We went to Easons and headed for the cookery section. Tommy had the name of the book written down on a piece of paper. He looked embarrassed as he handed it to the girl behind the counter.

"Are you Joan Curran's brother?" she asked.

"Yeah, I am."

"I went to school with her in Crumlin. I remember you used to be with her sometimes. What's she doing now?"

"She's in university, she's going to be a teacher."

"Oh, real posh. She was always a real brain box. And her brothers a bovver boy" she said, real smart.

She handed Tommy the book. I was fuming inside.

"Yeah, and you're working in Easons" I said as the two of us walked away. Tommy said to me under his breath "nice one Marty."

"Stuff her, she's just a jealous bitch. What was up with her?" I said.

We went past the GPO. There were posters all over the pillars "Brendan Grace's new single "Cushy Butterfield" in the shops now."

"Me sister went to see him. He's supposed to be real funny. He was born in Dublin" Tommy said.

Gilbert's new album, Back to Front out now.

"I'm getting that for Christmas" I said.

"What's yer man Bowie doin' now?" Tommy asked me.

"He has a new album coming out after Christmas I heard. He's tourin' in America. I hope he comes here someday."

We walked down Henry Street. It was packed with shoppers.

"I was havin' me break in work the other day" Tommy said " and I was reading the Reader's Digest and it said that someday you will have a machine in your house that will tape programmes off the televisions. Imagine you will be able to tape things when you're not there and then watch them later."

"You're joking" I said "the picture and all?"

"Yeah" Tommy said. "It will be much bigger than a normal tape. It said before the seventies are over they will be on sale everywhere. It's called videotaping."

"Fuckin' great" I said.

We went into a clothes shop. They had a whole section of crombie coats with velvet collars. The fellah behind the counter was staring at our clothes.

"Ten pound for Doc's" Tommy said. They were £5 in England.

"What di yi think of these?" Tommy said.

They were shirts with roundy collars instead of buttondown. "I think they're shite" I said.

They had a sign in the shop that said "Due to the bomb scare we may have to close suddenly."

"Due to the bomb scare I may have to shit in my pants suddenly more like" Tommy said.

The fellah didn't laugh. It was time to go.

"Let's go to Woolworths" I said.

I loved Woolworths upstairs café. We always were brought there on Christmas Eve when we were kids, after we had been to see Santa. Chips and a big fat sausage and beans. It was packed with people. We got a coke and chips each and sat in the corner, gawking at everyone. This old man was going around the tables begging. He came to our table. He smelt like the dump. "God Bless yi, boys, God bless yi."

Tommy said nothing. I knew he'd give him fuck all. I gave him 10 pence, seeing that I was almost a millionaire. His breath smelled like dog shite. How could someone go around like that I thought.

"I can't eat me chips now" Tommy said.

All around the walls were these pictures of Hawaiian beaches with the sun going down and lovely valleys with little houses with smoke coming out of the chimneys. Two men were up a ladder putting up Christmas decorations. There was a picture of John F Kennedy and Jackie Kennedy.

"Do yi remember when he was shot?" I said.

"Yeah" Tommy said "about 10 years ago wasn't it?"

"It was nine years ago the other day" I said. "I heard it on the telly. I remember that night" I said. "Me Ma and Da had gone out to some do and me and David and Joan were left on our own. We were watching some programme and someone came on and told us he had been shot and had died soon after. The next morning we were all having our breakfast and I said out of the blue "Ah yeah President Kennedy was shot dead last night". Me Ma's face dropped and Da nearly choked on his toast. Why didn't yi leave us a note so we'd know Ma said. Me Ma idolised him."

"So did mine" Tommy said.

"She started crying and turned on the radio" I said.

"I remember me, David and Joan all lookin' at each other like it's your fault, not it's yours. Yi know what I mean."

A few months before he was shot, my Ma and Peggy Ryan had gone out near the airport to see him and Jackie when they came to Dublin. My Ma said that they were so close he waved straight at them.

"I wonder did your man Oswald really do it?" Tommy said.

"My old man thinks the mafia killed him."

The sausages were lovely.

"Where are we goin' tonight?" Tommy asked.

"I dunno" I said "but me Ma and Da are goin' out tonight. Maybe we'll have a few gargles in the workshop."

Tommy looked happy coz the last thing he wanted was anyone drinking in his house. His Ma was a religious freak and hated drink.

"Tony and Des are callin' up to me about 7. I told Mick we'd meet him outside O'Hagans at half seven. I think I'll get some flagons" I said.

Two flagons and I get fairly gee-eyed, I thought. Mick was the best drinker. One night he drank two flagons of cider then a naggin of Vodka and he could still walk, and he only pissed once.

"Let's go" I said.

It was twelve o'clock. We went down Henry Street past the dealers. "Cheap mechanical toys." All selling loads of things that wind up. There were fellahs and girls everywhere. Some of them you'd recognise from the Loft although we hadn't been there for a few months. It was freezing out. I should have worn me crombie. We walked down Capel Street to a clothes shop. It had all the gear but most of it was shite. I loved going in because people always gawked at our clobber. They had music playing. *You wear it well* from Rod Stewart. I loved *Maggie May*. The first time we all took acid we were in Mick's house and his brother PJ had just bought it and played it about 20 times. Every time I heard a Rod Stewart song it reminded me of how out of our heads we were that night. God, we were stupid. People say that every time you took acid you killed some of your brain cells. I wonder. They had a whole rack of Tartan caps, with a big picture of Noddy Holder wearing one.

"Did yi see the posters of Slade on sale outside Easons?" Tommy said.

"No, where? Your man with the newspapers?"

"Yeah" Tommy said. "It's a full size poster of the four of them for 65p."

"Fuck, let's go and get one" I said. "I'll give it to Catherine. She'll love me for it."

"She does anyway" Tommy said.

I smiled.

"Yeah let's go."

Back down Henry Street and through the arcade. Buskers everywhere. These three skinheads were singing with a guitar each.

"Let's have a listen" I said.

They were singing *"Rockin' Robin"*, the Jacksons song. They were bleeding great. They had a small little plastic kids bucket and people were putting money in it.

"Fair play to them" I said. They had a little sign "Some skinheads just want to sing."

"I wish I could stand there and sing" Tommy said.

"Yeah and get money as well."

They saw the two of us and started singing *"Let your yeah be yeah"*. We both threw some change into the bucket. One of them nodded at us. When they stopped singing they started talking to us. They were from Killester and were starting a band. They had taken about £4 already.

"Move on boys."

This big culchie copper was telling us to move. One of the fellahs told him "We do requests Garda." He started playing "We'll we're off to Dublin in the Green, in the Green, with our helmets glistening in the sun."

"Now don't be smart you lot go on, feck off out of that."

Time to go. Tommy couldn't stop laughing. The copper didn't know what to do. He looked like it was his first day on the force. We said goodbye and walked around to O'Connell Street and Easons. I bought the poster and opened it to have a look. It was a complete life size poster of the four of them. Catherine loved Don Powell, the drummer. Noddy was my favourite. What a voice he had.

"She'll love this" I said. "I'll get me hole now."

Jaysus, did I say that, I thought to myself. Tommy said nothing but I knew what he was thinking.

"Don't end up like Des for fuck sake" he said.

"I'm only jokin'" I said. "We've never done it."

"All that time I thought he was joking too" said Tommy "but look how he's ended up. He's real moody lately, isn't he? We'll cheer him up tonight."

We headed for Fleet Street. I thought about the gang heading for the boat for Manchester. They would be all excited now, probably having a few pints before the game. A few gypsies were sitting on O'Connell Bridge begging. My

Ma had a knacker that called every Saturday afternoon and she was the only one Ma would give anything to. Before we could say anything this man took our picture and gave us a ticket.

"I'll get that during the week" I said."Get me one too" Tommy said.

We went back and told him we wanted another one. He gave Tommy a ticket as well. Everyone's Ma and Da had a picture of themselves in the same spot walking across O'Connell Bridge. Fleet Street was packed as usual. I used to love coming into town with Ma at Christmas and going into every toy shop. Then in somewhere for chips and sausages. They were always nicer than the ones your Ma made. Ma and Da would tell us how much was going to be spent on each of us so you had it all figured out in your head what you could get. Last year, because I had left school, I got £5. I kept it until after Christmas and bought Gilbert's album "*Himself*". We went down the back of the bus and lit up. The bus was packed with shoppers and their kids.

"Imagine if Mick makes it in England" I said. "I wonder what the money will be like."

"Mick reckons Kevin Keegan gets over £200 a week."

"Jaysus, for kickin' a bleedin' ball around" Tommy said.

"Imagine us in the VIP seats watchin' him play" he said.

"Yeah, just bring us the gargle missus and the cigars, fuck the match" I said. "The gang of us, pissed, making a show of him, then getting ejected from the ground."

Tommy was laughing to himself. "Or bringin' in our own flagons with us. Remember your man on the boat with the clothes" Tommy said. When we went to see United play Derby in September, there was a young skinhead on the boat going over with the worst rags on you ever saw. When he got to Manchester he bought heaps of clothes in one shop and put them on and threw all his clothes in a litter bin outside the shop. Even his boots. When the game was over and we were all back in the city getting something to eat, his boots were still sticking out of the top of the bin. He went to the game with all his new clobber on looking like someone on their Confirmation day. He stood out like a real gobshite.

"Sometimes we stick out like a bleedin' sore thumb" Tommy said.

"What di yi mean?" I said.

"The Irish, you'd know us a mile away sometimes."

"I know what yi mean" I said.

He is right I thought. There were times when I was in England when I didn't want people to hear my accent.

"Every time you look at UTV or the BBC there's some smart arse makin' jokes about the Irish" Tommy said. "Yi never see us on the TV crackin' jokes about them, do yi?"

"My old man says the joke is on them though" I said. "They're left with Northern Ireland and all the shite that goes with it and the English people are paying for it all with their taxes."

Crumlin Village. We got off the bus and walked up by the church. There was a wedding on. They were standing outside and they all looked freezing. We stood and had a gawk. There was a gang of kids hanging around waiting for a "grushie". The groom threw a handful of money at them and they all jumped all over the place, pushing each other out of the way. It was so funny to watch.

"I'll give yi a shout at seven Tommy" I said.

"Ok."

Unbelievable, there's nobody at home. I had the house to myself. That meant one thing. Music. I stuck Bowie on. Joan's boyfriend had given me a loan of Hunky Dory. It was magic. My favourite track was *Queen Bitch*. I picked up David's guitar and imagined I was Bowie. *"Ba Ba Coo Ba Coo Ba Bam."* I was on stage at the National Stadium. *"Well I'm up on the eleventh floor and I'm watchin' the cruisers below."* Brilliant. I had all the actions. I had seen him on the Old Grey Whistle Test and on Top of the Pops. *"She's so swishy in her satin and tat, in her frock coat and bipetty, bopetty hat, I could do better than that..."* Then *Life on Mars*. *"It's a God awful small affair, to the girl with the mousey hair."* It must be great to stand up in front of thousands of people and perform. I was singing at the top of my voice now. *"Oh man, look at those cavemen go. It's the freakiest show..."* I'd love to see him someday. I stuck on a few singles. *"Mama we're all crazy now."* I was Noddy now. Really getting stuck into it. *"I don't want to drink my whiskey like you do..."* In walks Derek along with his pal Paul.

"Ha ha, you were dancin'."

The two of them started laughing hysterically. The little shites. How long were they standing behind me?

"We're gonna tell everyone" he said.

"Ok. How much?" I asked.

"10p each."

"Ok."

I looked out the window and they were still laughing all the way to the end of the road. You couldn't see their arses for dust. Fuck it, I was really enjoying that. They must have sneaked in. I put on a slowey. It was one of Joan's favourites. "So far Away" by Carole King. I like that song. It's sad but nice. Joan got Carole King's album Tapestry last Christmas. God, she had some other shite. John Mayall. Who the fuck is he? And Fairport Convention. Jaysus.

I went into the back room and turned on the tele. Horse racing. The fire needed cleaning out so I got the paper and took out the ashes. I may as well light it I thought. Up to the workshop for some sticks and coal. In that few minutes Derek and his pal were back already from the shops, sprawled on the floor watching tele. A Lassie movie was on. They both had little bags of sweets. Derek always amazed me at how much he could get for 10p.

I went upstairs and decided to have a good look through my clothes. I had loads of clobber now. A pair of Doc's boots, a pair of Doc's shoes, a pair of loafers and loads of socks, black ones of course. Two Ben Sherman check shirts and a button-down black shirt with a white tie. Harrington jacket, crombie coat and a Wrangler denim jacket. Wrangler jeans, turned up and six different pairs of trousers. My favourite pair were the turned up Oxford bags. Yes, I had a complete suedeheads wardrobe. In the back of the wardrobe I still had some of my old clothes. Levi cream coloured cords and a jacket to match from when I was 14. A pair of brown monkey boots from last year. A black duffel coat also from last year with those wooden buttons that looked like bullets. In the very back was my pride and joy. A pair of hipster bell-bottoms in black with four huge buttons. They were by 13th birthday present.

I started laughing. I remember I had a pair of winkle picker boots, the bell-bottoms and a white polo neck jumper. Jaysus, I looked funny. At the time I thought I was the bees knees but looking back I looked like a tall dogshite. Tonight with the gang I'll wear denim, black shirt and black brogues. I went downstairs. It was a quarter to five. The soccer results were coming in on the funny typewriter across the screen. Man Utd 2 Southampton 1. Yes. United won. Dad came in. He had a black suit under his arm for the do that night.

"Will I start the tea Da?"

"Yeah" said Derek.

"I didn't ask you."

"Yeah, do that Marty. We have to go out early."

I put the grill on. Amazing when you put food on everyone appears from nowhere. David, Joan and then Ma in from work. It was all go. Ma and Da getting ready. David getting ready for a party he was going to. I made an executive decision. I loved saying that to myself. Ma always says it when she has something to announce to the family. I'll give them all their tea on a plate and shag setting the table.

"Good idea, Marty" Ma said.

Ma and Da had to get to the community hall by half past six to catch the bus.

"Where's the do on Ma?" I asked.

"Out in Portmarnock. We won't be home until the early hours" she said. "Derek is staying in Paul's house."

"I'm going to a party in Harold's Cross with Alice and two of her friends" David said.

"Well, whoever is in or out make sure the house is locked up and no coming in too late."

"Where are you goin' Marty?" Da asked.

Joan never gets asked I thought. Can't do anything wrong.

"I'm meeting Catherine and we're goin' to the flix" I lied.

Bollox I thought. It was going to be a big night. The Generation Game was on the tele. These four gobshites had to laugh like the laughing policeman.

"What some people do for a bleedin' cuddly toy" Da said.

It was embarrassing. "Let's have a look at the old scoreboard." Brucey was funny enough though, with his big long chin. Nobody missed the Generation Game on Saturday evening. The doorbell rang. In came Tom and Peggy Ryan, all done up for the do. Tom had a suit and dickie bow. Da came downstairs with his suit and dickie bow as well.

"Aren't they lovely" Peggy said.

"Let's have a quick one before we go."

The sherries came out.

"I see Manchester won Marty" Tom said.

"Yeah, they did Mister Ryan."

"Who scored?"

"I know Ted MacDougall got one, I don't know who got the other."

"Great."

"Ok. Let's go. See yis tomorrow."

"Have a great time Ma" Joan said.

"We will."

Ma was forty but she only looked thirty. Off they went.

"I bags the bathroom first" Joan said and ran up the stairs.

The doorbell rang again. It was Derek's pal Paul and his mother to bring him to their house for the night. Off he went with his bag of toys, bottle of Taylor Keith and his teddy bear. He was delighted with himself. Me, David and Joan left in the house. Now what was Joan doing tonight? Would I have the house to myself? It was nearly seven. Joan was finished in the bathroom. I got in before David. A quick wash and into my clobber. We all had to meet at seven thirty. Alice called with another couple and David headed off to his party. Just Joan and me. Ah, fuck it, I'll come back later on and if she's here, she's here.

"See yi later Joan."

"See yi."

"I won't be too late" I said.

It was nearly half seven. Shit, it was cold. I was singing *"You're so Vain"* to myself. It was on Top of the Pops the other night. She was a fine thing, Carly Simon. Loads of little groups of women were heading off to the Bingo in the Apollo Cinema. They didn't show many films there anymore, not like when we were kids. We used to love going on Friday nights. It was always packed. About three years ago they showed "The Good, the bad and the Ugly". It was over 18 but Da took me and David and gave the bouncer on the door twenty cigarettes and he let us all in. It was a great movie. A real long one. The music was great. Des, Mick, Tony and Tommy were all waiting. All dressed up to the nines.

"How yis going?"

"Ok" said Mick.

"I need some fags" I said. "Twenty Major Mr O'Hagan."

"Off to the Bingo Marty?" Mr O'Hagan asked with that smile on his face.

"Ah yeah" I said. "Two fat ladies. Now do I look like I'm dressed for Bingo Mr O'Hagan?"

"I suppose not" he said laughing.

"Thanks. See yi."

"Ok boys, what's it gonna be?"

"Let's get some gargle first" Des said. "We'll go up to the Submarine Bar off Licence."

"Yeah and who the fuck will go in?" Tony asked.

"I will" Mick said.

"We'll do the party thing. " Ok"? I said.

This worked for us before. You write your order down on a piece of paper with an address and say your Ma and Da sent you down because they were having a party.

"Ok. I'm havin' two flagons" Mick said.

"Me too" said Tony.

"I'll have a naggin of vodka and a bottle of Club Orange" Des said.

Tommy wanted his usual half dozen Harp.

"I'll have a naggin of vodka with a bottle of Coke" I said.

Mick had a bit of bum fluff under his nose so he looked the oldest. Off we went.

"Joan should be goin' out so do yis want to come back to the garage?"

I didn't have to ask twice.

"Yeah. Great" Des said.

Our garage was attached to Da's workshop and there was loads of room. We waited around the corner and Mick went in with a heap of change from all of us. He always put on a deep voice. Once he went in with a cap on and a newspaper under his arm to really look the part. We all waited without saying anything.

Five minutes later Mick appeared with a big box full of gargle. We headed off back towards my house. Tony and Mick put their flagons under their crombies. Myself and Des stuck the vodka down our jeans. Tommy just held his half dozen under his arm, still in the brown paper bag.

"Later on, remind me to tell yis a story" I said.

"And I've got somethin' to show yis too" Des said.

"Ok" said Mick.

I decided to tell them all about Nevin.

"Tell us now yi bollox" Des said.

"No, just wait" I said.

"Yeah, we're in for an exciting evening" Mick said. "Des is gonna show us his mickey."

We all started laughing.

"and Marty's gonna tell us about his."

He's a funny prick, I thought to myself. We had our drinks so everyone was happy but I knew in the back of my mind that Des would get sad after he had a few drinks. Mick and Tony were carrying their flagons like they had babies under their coats.

"Bollox" said Mick.

A squad car passed right by us. The brake lights went on. The five of us dashed up the side lane at the library. If they caught us they'd take all the gargle and probably charge us. Trying to run with the vodka down my jeans was a bollox. We went half way down the lane and then down another one. Alan Kirwan was kicking a ball outside his garage door.

"Alan, your garage for a minute" I said. "We'll pay yi."

Before he could say anything we all bundled in, closed the door and turned off the light. I knew Alan from school. He was Ok.

"We'll give you 10p each Ok."

Everyone whispered Ok. We didn't make a sound. About a minute later we heard "The little fuckers, where did they go?" " Where does this lane lead to"? Another voice. "There's a field at one end and the old graveyard is at the other end. They must have had either drink or drugs. Did you recognise any of them Paul?" "No Tom. I didn't. We'll drive down the village."

We could hear them walking off. Mick let a little fart. The six of us pissed ourselves laughing. It was pitch black.

"Oh yi smelly bastard" Des said.

I lit up a Major. We turned the lights back on.

"Jaysus, thanks Alan" I said. "Is your Ma and Da in."

"Naw, they've gone to that dance in Portmarnock."

"So have mine and Tommy's" I said.

"Can I drink a flagon here Alan?" Mick said.

"Yeah. Why not?"

Great. We all gave him 10p. He went into the house and got a glass for Des and me and an opener for Tommy. There were paint cans everywhere, so we sat on them. I loved vodka and coke. Mick gave Alan a swig of his flagon.

"What are yi doing now Alan?" I asked.

"I'm on my second year as an electrician at Guinness's."

"Are yi? That's good." I said.

I wasn't really that interested but we were in his garage after all.

"Are yis goin' to a dance?" he asked.

"Naw, probably not. We might go back to my house, if me sister goes out."

"Is that Joan?" he said.

"Yeah, that's her."

"Me brother has the hots for her."

"Has he? He's wastin' his time" I said. "She's been goin' with Eamon for nearly two years."

"Di yi want some ice for that Marty?"

"Why not?"

He went back down to the house. Tony looked at me. He was smiling.

"Yeah and bring us a few sandwiches as well."

That was it. We were off.

"Turkey, preferably" I said.

We were trying to talk and laughing at the same time.

"And five cups of tea" Des came in with.

The tears were rolling down our faces.

"And have yi any sisters?" Mick said. "If not your Ma will do."

Des had snots coming out of his nose now. Alan came back with a Tupperware thing full of ice. We stopped laughing. At least tried to. The drink was starting to kick in. Mick was nearly finished his flagon. Des let a monstrous belch.

"We'll wait about another fifteen minutes and we'll go, OK?"

"Ok" they said.

I felt like James Bond with the glass of vodka, coke and ice. Tommy was on his third bottle. Kirwan wasn't a skinhead or suedehead but his older brother was a bit of a hippy with the denim jeans and jacket with patches all over them. Tommy gave him a bottle of Harp. Miracles never cease, I thought. Alan was in his element now.

"Take a look at this" he said.

He stood on a paint can and rummaged on top of a load of timber stacked up against a wall. He took down a little wooden box and opened it. Well would you believe it? A little stash of Bob Hope.

"Ah, no" said Mick. "It's bleedin' months since I've had any of this."

He rolled a huge joint, lit it and passed it around. Mick was taking huge drags out of it. My head was spinning. It was only nine o'clock now and still loads of night left. Des was real quiet now. He was staring into space biting his lip.

"What have yi got to show us Des?" I asked.

He took an envelope out of his crombie. It was from Elaine. He passed around a photograph of her. She had gone into a photo booth in Melbourne and pulled up her jumper and you could see her fat belly. Our Baby was written on her stomach with a marker. She had a big smile on her face. It was weird.

"When is it due Des?" I said for something to say.

"In February, the first week."

"That's great isn't it" Mick said "that she could send you that."

He had a letter from her as well.

"It took two weeks to come from Australia" Des said. I could see he was still really sad.

"Will we go?" Mick said.

"Ok."

"Leave the empties. I'll get rid of them in the field."

"Thanks Alan" I said.

The five of us stood out in the laneway. Alan closed the garage door.

"See yis."

"Yeah, thanks Alan."

"We owe yi one."

There was a huge moon and the laneway was all bright like.

"I'm fuckin' starving" Tommy said. "Let's go to the chipper."

"Yeah. OK."

We all headed off still with our gargle hidden under our clothes but feeling much braver now. We were waking five abreast now just like the old times. Time for song. *"Can yi still recall, in the juke box hall when the music played. And the world sang loud to a brand new sound in those far off days."* We were all in full voice now. *"Rock and Roll, Rock and Roll"*. I hadn't smoked dope for about six months. I was flying. The chipper hadn't been open that long and they were still getting ready for the mad rush later in the night when the pubs closed. It was only half nine. I ordered a spice burger and chips. We sat outside the chipper on a little wall and stuffed our faces. Tony had a leg of chicken in one hand and chips in the other.

"So what's your story Marty?" Mick said.

"Ok."

I told them the whole story, no lies. They couldn't believe it. Tommy thought it was the best story he'd heard in years.

"He deserved it" Des said. "He's a horrible bollox."

Then we started laughing.

"I'd love to have seen it" Tony said.

The pubs were starting to fill up and we could hear the singing coming out of them.

"Someday we'll all be in there drinkin' instead of in fuckin' fields and lanes" Mick said.

"Naw, you'll be in some big fancy hotel in Liverpool drinkin'" Tommy said.

"Yeah, what's happening" Tony asked.

"I've got to wait until January and then go over for about ten days or so with me Da. I'll have to play a load of games with the Juniors and they watch yi all the time."

"Jaysus' yi must be real excited" I said.

"I am. They even put yi up in a hotel but I'm real nervous as well" Mick said.

We were getting real brave now and taking our drinks out from under our coats. Des was getting really pissed. His eyes were going all over the place.

"C'mon, let's see if there's anyone at my house" I said.

We all staggered off down past the butchers, past O'Hagans and around the back way, through the old orchard to my house. I looked over the wall and could see no lights on. I climbed over and opened the workshop door.

"No fuckin' noise now" I said.

"Stay here" Tony said. "Your Da has a radio."

The workshop was full of timber and saw-dust but there were loads of places to sit. We turned on the radio and tuned into Radio Luxembourg. The reception was great. *"Tumblin' Dice"* from the Rolling Stones was playing. I love the Stones. They bring back so many memories of when I was young. Back into the gargle. Des just didn't look happy.

"I've been thinkin' about Canada" Tony said. "He's definitely goin' next year and if I don't go I'll be out of a job."

"Jaysus, Canada" I said. "You'd be real homesick" I said.

"Yeah, but me Ma thinks it's a great opportunity that'll only come once."

Then Des said something really funny.

"Yeah, like me. I only came once and look how my life has changed."

We all laughed sort of nervously then we couldn't stop. We'd never really talked about him doing it or anything like that.

"Had yi not got a Johnny on, Des?" Mick asked.

"Naw, she said she couldn't get pregnant because it was that time of the month, yi know what I mean. And once yi stick it in it's very hard to take it out again."

He smiled.

"Especially when it's very hard" I said.

More laughs. At least we had him laughing I thought.

"For fuck sake Tony, don't do that."

Tony flicked a cigarette butt into the sawdust.

"Ah Jaysus sorry Marty."

He poured some of his second flagon over it and put it out.

"It'll always be your kid Des" I said.

"I've no doubt that it will all work out somehow."

"Me Ma always says that" I said.

Des was looking a bit happier.

"For fuck sake don't leave any bottles lying around" I said.

We were all getting really pissed now. It was eleven o'clock. "I love this song" Tommy said. *"The young New Mexican puppeteer..."* Tom Jones, we were off. *"He saw the people all lived in fear, he thought that maybe they'd listen to a puppet telling them what to do..."*

"Shush for fuck sake" I said. "One of the neighbours will tell me Da."

Des looked really pissed now. He belched straight at my face and the smell of fucking gargle, onion rings and cigarettes was enough to make me puke.

"I'm gonna be sick." And I was. All into the sawdust.

"Ah fuck I'm sorry" Des said.

"It looks good though" Tony said, looking at the puke mixed in with the sawdust, sort of like a chicken curry.

The rest of them were all laughing but I puked again. Tony grabbed a shovel and scooped it all up and went out the lane and threw it over the wall into the old orchard. I wiped my mouth with an old rag and lit up a major.

"I'm sorry Marty" Des said.

"Not your fault Des. A big fry, vodka and coke, spice burger and chips and dope doesn't mix too well" I said.

The five of us had a slash against the wall in the laneway. We threw all our bottles into the orchard. It was time for a walk. I locked the garage, making sure everything looked OK. The five of us headed down the lane and back towards the village. All in a line. I loved this. We were all together. It had been a great year since I left school. Drink, drugs, Manchester United, girlfriend, great clothes, a job and money. All in a little over a year. I hoped this would go on for ever but I knew it probably wouldn't. In a few months Tony could be gone to Canada, Mick to Liverpool and God knows what Des will do. That could leave me and misery guts Tommy. But I had Catherine and I loved her. It was midnight. We sat at O'Hagans and watched the world go by. It was bleeding cold but we didn't care. Some oul' one was murdering *"My Way"* in the pub. We were all listening, saying nothing.

"Your Ma hasn't much of a voice" Mick said to Tommy.

We were all laughing again, even Tommy. She stopped, there was applause and then she was off again. "Pleeese release me let me goooo" Tony ran over to the pub and shouted at the top of his voice through an open window "Yi can't sing for shite, missus" and then ran like fuck along with the rest of us through the village trying to laugh and run at the same time. It wasn't easy, especially when you're a bit pissed. We stopped in the church car park. The tears were rolling down my face.

"Yi bollox Tony. You're fuckin' mad" I said.

We sat outside the boy scout hall, lit up a fag and stayed there for over an hour just talking about the last year or two and all the things we had got up to. Apart from what happened to Des it had all been nothing but fun.

"I wonder what the fuck we'll all be doing in the year 2000" Tony said.

"I'll be 44 I said. Probably loads of kids, and a big fat beer belly."

"Naw, I bet the world will have ended by then" Tommy said. "Someone will have dropped the bomb."

"Like now" Tony said and he let a huge fart.

I looked at them all laughing and wondered what we would all be doing in the year 2000. Me Da still talks about all his pals when he was my age and he is 42. The best years of your life he always says. It was nearly half past one. We made our usual arrangements for tomorrow morning then we all scattered our own ways. I walked with Tony and Tommy through the church gate and up our road.

"See yis tomorrow."

I sneaked in the door. Joan and Eamon were in the kitchen, drinking coffee and listening to Leonard Cohen on her tape recorder. I said hello and goodbye and went up to bed. David wasn't in yet so I put my tranny on low and got under the blankets. The sheets were freezing. Shit, I jumped out and ran into Ma and Da's bedroom and put on their electric blanket. They'll love me for doing that. I lay back in bed thinking, Radio Luxembourg playing in the background. Tony Prince. Johnny Nash was singing "There are more questions than answers". I had a great night. I'll tell Catherine all about it tomorrow. My eyes were closing. Bowie was looking down at me from the wall. Maybe he'll come to Ireland someday. There was talk that Slade were coming after Christmas.

I hoped this would go on forever. I loved being with Tommy, Tony, Des and Mick. We were all different but together we had great fun. I knew in the back of my mind it would all end someday and we'll all go our own ways. Coming home from work a few weeks ago I read in the New Musical Express about Don McLean's American Pie and about how sad he was when Buddy Holly died and something really special to him was all over and gone. I sort of know what he meant when he said *"and there we all were in one place, a generation lost in space, with no time left to start again.*

The End

Glossary

A "Mill"	A fight
Another "go"	Another fight
Bob Hope	Marijuana, hash etc
Clobber	Clothes
Culchies	Nickname for person born in any county out of Dublin
Diddys	Bosom, breasts
Dub	Person born in Dublin
Flagon	Flagon bottle of Cider
Getting his hole	Having sex
Getting his wear	Kissing
Gink	Fool, Idiot, Dope
Gosh	Money
Gutties	Hooligans
Jacks	Toilet
Janey Mack	Exclamation like Oh my God
Mickey	Penis
Mot	A girl, girlfriend
Mush	Face
Oul One	Older woman
Slag	Make a fool of
Slash	Urinate